CANADIAN CURRICULUM PRESS
Forward Learning

Written by teachers working in the Canadian cla

Math

3

$$423 - 139 = 284$$

$$765 + 476 = 1241$$

$$28 \div 4 = 7$$

$$5 \times 7 = 35$$

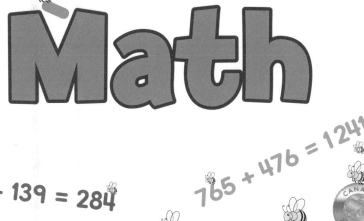

- Addition, subtraction, multiplication, division
- Fractions
- Canadian money and time
- Geometry, graphs and probability
- And much more!

Elaine J. Kenny, B.Ed.

Grade 3 Math

Contents

Number Order

Print the numbers in order from least to greatest.

426, 725, 619, 443   _426_, _443_, _619_, _725_

673, 947, 813, 999   _____, _____, _____, _____

311, 342, 421, 299   _____, _____, _____, _____

703, 698, 896, 799   _____, _____, _____, _____

812, 99, 999, 499   _____, _____, _____, _____

Print the missing numbers. Watch for skip counting!

114 _115_ 116 _____ _____ 119 _____ _____ 122 _____

402 _____ 404 _____ 406 _____ _____ 409 _____ 411

667 _____ _____ 670 _____ _____ 673 _____ 675

310 320 _____ _____ 350 _____ _____ 380 _____ _____

940_____ 944 _____ _____ 950 _____ _____ 956 _____

2

Thousands, Hundreds, Tens, and Ones

Example:

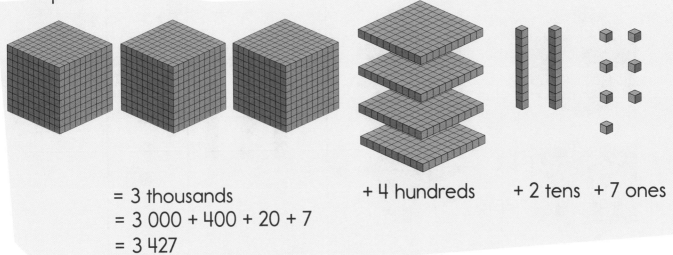

= 3 thousands
= 3 000 + 400 + 20 + 7
= 3 427

+ 4 hundreds   + 2 tens + 7 ones

Count and print the number of thousands, hundreds, tens, and ones on the lines below.

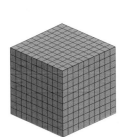 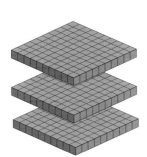 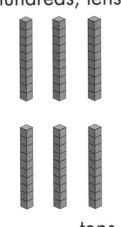 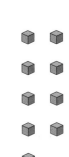

= _____ thousands + _____ hundreds + _____ tens + _____ ones

= _____ + _____ + _____ + _____

= _____

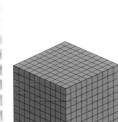 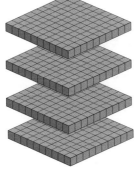 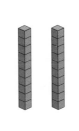 

= _____ thousands + _____ hundreds + _____ tens + _____ ones

= _____ + _____ + _____ + _____

= _____

Number Sense and Numeration

Thousands, Hundreds, Tens, and Ones

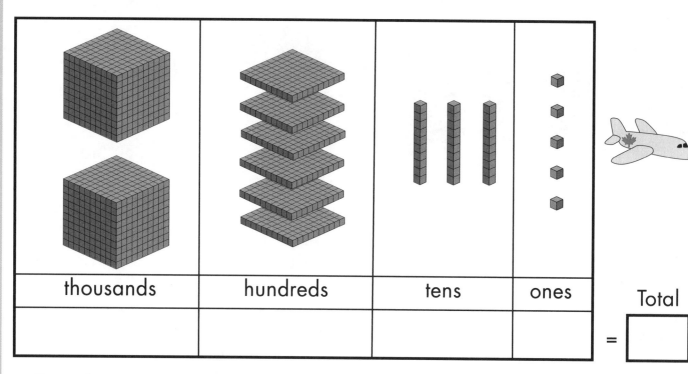

thousands	hundreds	tens	ones	Total
				=

Follow the instructions for each number.

6 23① Circle the ones.

4 156 Circle the tens.

3 915 Circle the hundreds.

8 121 Circle the thousands.

1 546 Circle the hundreds.

5 767 Circle the thousands.

9 000 Circle the tens.

1 111 Circle the hundreds.

What is the place value of the **green** digit? Circle the answer.

1 693	thousands	hundreds	tens	ones
4 794	thousands	hundreds	tens	ones
6 111	thousands	hundreds	tens	ones
9 423	thousands	hundreds	tens	ones
4 199	thousands	hundreds	tens	ones
3 660	thousands	hundreds	tens	ones

Expanded Notation

Example:
Expanded notation using **words**.
4 872 = 4 thousands + 8 hundreds + 7 tens + 2 ones

Example:
Expanded notation using **digits.**
4 872 = 4000 + 800 + 70 + 2

Use **words** to show the numbers in expanded notation.

693 = _____6 hundreds_____ + _____ + _____

1 314 = _____ + _____ + _____ + _____

4 643 = _____ + _____ + _____ + _____

798 =_____ + _____ + _____

Use **digits** to show the numbers in expanded notation.

451 = _____400_____ + _____ + _____

1 846 = _____ + _____ + _____ + _____

4 970 = _____ + _____ + _____ + _____

323 = _____ + _____ + _____

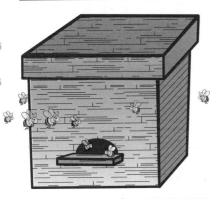

5

Addition Without Regrouping

When we add, we find the sum. First we add the ones, then the tens, and then the hundreds.

Add the ones:

```
  3 2 5
+ 2 6 1
      6
```

Next add the tens:

```
  3 2 5
+ 2 6 1
    8 6
```

Next add the hundreds:

```
  3 2 5
+ 2 6 1
  5 8 6
```

Try these.

```
  1 2 6          4 6          6 8
+ 3 5 2        + 3 3        + 2 1
```

```
  3 1 1          1 3 2          6 3 1
+ 4 6 7        + 2 2 5        + 3 2 4
```

Addition With Regrouping

When the sum in any column is greater than 9, we need to regroup that number. See how this works in this example:

```
  1
  7 8
+ 5 6
    4
```

We add the ones column, 8+6=14. Since 14 is greater than 9, we have to regroup it into 1 ten and 4 ones. We put the 4 ones into the ones place and the 1 ten into the tens place.

```
1 1
  7 8
+ 5 6
  3 4
```

Now we add the tens, 1+7+5=13. We have to regroup the 13 tens into 1 hundred and 3 tens. We put the 3 tens into the tens place and the 1 hundred into the hundreds place.

```
1 1
  7 8
+ 5 6
1 3 4
```

Finally we add the hundreds. 1+0=1. We have found the sum, 134.

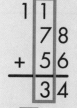

Hint: Be sure to keep the numbers lined up in the right place value column.

Add:

```
   25              26             156            816
 + 36            + 48           + 27           + 159
```

```
   78              71             321            267
 + 15            + 19           + 88           + 247
```

```
   43              84             477            699
 + 48            + 17           + 183          + 128
```

```
   75              37             765            575
 + 25            + 57           + 476          + 426
```

```
  32        31        15        33        85
 +88       +79       +98       +97       +69
```

```
  39        89        24        85        82
 +84       +58       +96       +97       +48
```

```
  43        49        51        95        91
 +67       +94       +69       +99       +87
```

Subtraction Without Regrouping

When we subtract, we find the difference. First we subtract the ones, then the tens, and then the hundreds.

$$
\begin{array}{r}
7\,5\,\boxed{9} \\
-2\,4\,\boxed{3} \\
\hline
\boxed{6}
\end{array}
\qquad
\begin{array}{r}
7\,\boxed{5}\,9 \\
-2\,\boxed{4}\,3 \\
\hline
\boxed{1}\,6
\end{array}
\qquad
\begin{array}{r}
\boxed{7}\,5\,9 \\
-\boxed{2}\,4\,3 \\
\hline
\boxed{5}\,1\,6
\end{array}
$$

Try these.

$$
\begin{array}{r}
1\,9 \\
-1\,7 \\
\hline
\end{array}
\qquad
\begin{array}{r}
5\,6 \\
-2\,1 \\
\hline
\end{array}
\qquad
\begin{array}{r}
3\,3 \\
-1\,2 \\
\hline
\end{array}
$$

$$
\begin{array}{r}
9\,8 \\
-7\,4 \\
\hline
\end{array}
\qquad
\begin{array}{r}
8\,6 \\
-5\,5 \\
\hline
\end{array}
\qquad
\begin{array}{r}
4\,6 \\
-1\,4 \\
\hline
\end{array}
$$

Subtraction With Regrouping

When we subtract, sometimes we have to regroup. See how this works in this example.

$$
\begin{array}{r}
4\,\boxed{5} \\
-\,2\,\boxed{7} \\
\hline
\end{array}
$$

We start with the ones. Since we can't subtract 7 from 5, we need to regroup. We take 1 ten from the tens place and add it to the 5 ones so that we now have 15 ones and 3 tens.

Now we can subtract the ones column, 15-7=8.

Next, we subtract the tens column.

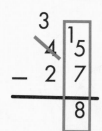

Since we regrouped 1 ten away from the 4 tens, there are 3 tens left. We subtract 3-2=1. Now we have found the difference, 18.

Number Sense and Numeration

Subtract:

1. 355
   −143

2. 725
   −412

3. 967
   −132

4. 186
   −169

5. 890
   −271

6. 579
   −176

7. 618
   −332

8. 644
   −427

9. 399
   −386

10. 378
    −298

11. 467
    −121

12. 471
    −330

Subtraction

Add and subtract to solve the word problems.

Jeff has 363 hockey cards and Jake has 193 hockey cards.

a. How many hockey cards do the boys have in all?

_____ hockey cards

b. How many more hockey cards does Jeff have than Jake?

_____ more

Rohan has 423 buttons. Jamari has 96 fewer buttons then Jamari.

a. How many buttons does Jamari have?

_____ buttons

b. How many buttons do the boys have in all?

_____ buttons

Look at the cost of skates.
a. What is the price difference between the skates? $ _____

b. What is the total cost of both pairs of skates? $ _____

Multiplication

Multiplication is a way to add numbers faster. Multiplication is adding the same number together multiple times. When numbers are multiplied, the answer is called the **product**.

Example:

How many scoops of ice cream are there?

$$3 + 3 + 3 + 3 = 12$$
4 groups of 3 scoops = 12
$$4 \times 3 = 12$$

__3__ + __3__ + __3__ + __3__ = __12__

Complete the addition and multiplication sentences.

How many petals?

__ + __ + __ = ____
__ groups of 5 petals = ____
__ × __ = ____
There are __ petals.

How many bees?

__ + __ + __ + __ + __ + __ = ____
____ groups of 2 bees = ____
__ × __ = ____
There are __ bees.

How many ladybugs?

__ + __ + __ + __ + __ = ____
__groups of 4 ladybugs = ____
__ × __ = ____
There are __ ladybugs.

How many butterflies?

             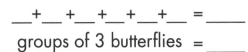 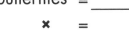

__ + __ + __ + __ + __ = ____
____ groups of 3 butterflies = ____
__ × __ = ____
There are __ butterflies.

Multiplication

Look at the pictures. Fill in the blanks.

__4__ groups of __8__ crayons

    = __4__ x __8__

    = __32__

___ groups of ___ pennies

    = ___ x ___

    = ___

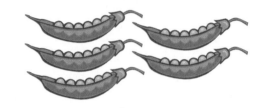 

___ groups of ___ peas in pod

    = ___ x ___

    = ___

___ groups of ___ beans

    = ___ x ___

    = ___

Write a multiplication sentence to match each group of beads.

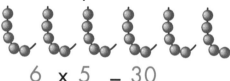 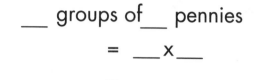

__6__ x __5__ = __30__

___ x ___ = ___

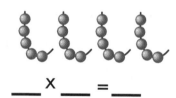 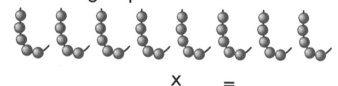

___ x ___ = ___

___ x ___ = ___

Practice multiplication tables.

1 x 2 =___	1 x 5 =___	1 x 3 =___	1 x 7 =___
2 x 2 =___	2 x 5 =___	2 x 3 =___	2 x 7 =___
3 x 2 =___	3 x 5 =___	3 x 3 =___	3 x 7 =___
4 x 2 =___	4 x 5 =___	4 x 3 =___	4 x 7 =___
5 x 2 =___	5 x 5 =___	5 x 3 =___	5 x 7 =___
6 x 2 =___	6 x 5 =___	6 x 3 =___	6 x 7 =___
7 x 2 =___	7 x 5 =___	7 x 3 =___	7 x 7 =___

Division

Division is equal sharing or grouping. The answer to the question is called a **quotient**.

Example:
How many baseballs in all? __20__
How many groups are there? __4__
This shows 20 ÷ 4 = 5

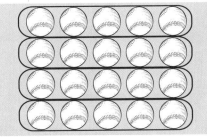

How many are there in total? _____
You can eat 3 apples a day.
Circle groups of 3.
How many groups are there? _____
How many days will it take you
to eat all the apples? _____
Write a division sentence.

_____

How many are there in total? _____
You can put 4 balls in each bin.
Circle groups of 4.
How many groups are there? _____
How many bins do you need? _____
Write a division sentence.

_____

How many are there in total? _____
You want to give 2 each to some friends.
Circle in groups of 2.
How many groups of 2? _____
How many friends can you give
2 marbles to? Write a division sentence.

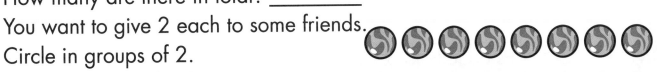

_____

Division

Draw the equal groupings. Fill in the blanks. The first one is done.

Divide 20 pencils equally among 4 backpacks.

There are ___5___ pencils in each backpack.

20 ÷ 4 = ___5___

Hint: Draw one pencil at a time in each backpack. Count as you go until you have drawn 20 pencils.

Divide 15 frogs equally onto 5 lilypads.

There are _____ frogs on each lilypad.

15 ÷ 5 = _____

Divide 12 oranges equally into 4 bowls.

There are _____ oranges in each bowl.

12 ÷ 4 = _____

Divide 12 balloons equally to 3 children.

Each child has _____ balloons.

12 ÷ 3 = _____

Fractions

Fractions tell about equal parts of a whole or set.

$$\frac{2}{5} \quad \textbf{Numerator}$$
Denominator

There are 5 parts to this whole. 2 parts are shaded.

The **denominator** is the bottom number in a fraction. It tells how many parts there are in total in the whole or set. In this case the denominator is 5. The **numerator** is the top number in a fraction. It is the number of equal parts being identified. In this case the numerator is 2.

The line separating the numerator and denominator means 'out of'. This fraction is $\frac{2}{5}$. It means 2 equal parts 'out of' 5 total parts.

Pizza Parts

Look at the pizza.
Some slices have pepperoni,
some have mushrooms,
some have olives,
and some are plain.

Answer the questions
about the parts of the pizza.

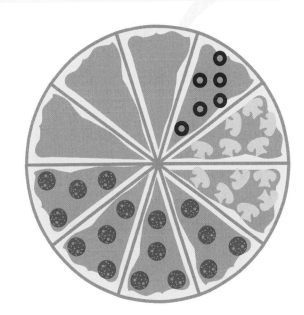

1. How many slices of pizza are there in total? _____

2. What fraction of the pizza is plain? _____

3. What fraction has pepperoni? _____

4. What fraction has olives? _____

5. What fraction has mushrooms? _____

Fractions

Write a fraction that identifies the coloured part of each shape.

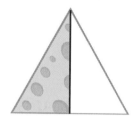
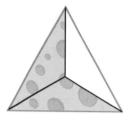

$$\frac{1}{2}$$

_____   _____   _____

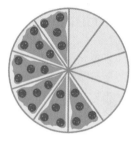
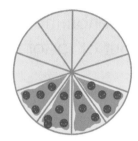
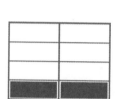
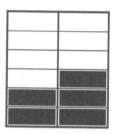

_____   _____   _____   _____

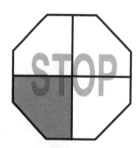

_____   _____   _____   _____

_____   _____   _____   _____

Number Sense and Numeration

Canadian Money

$5.00	$2.00	$1.00	25¢	10¢	5¢	1¢

Circle the money that adds up to the amount in the box.

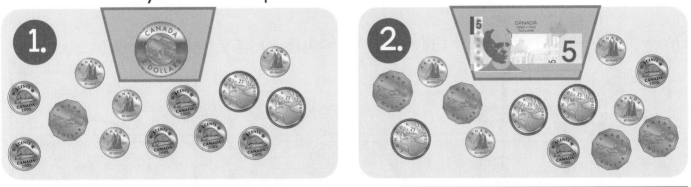

Estimate how much money each child has. Write your estimate on the line.
Count the actual amount. Write it on the line.

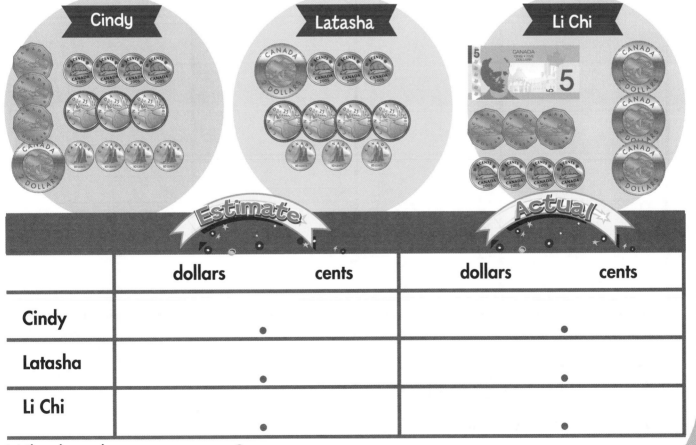

	Estimate		Actual	
	dollars	cents	dollars	cents
Cindy				
Latasha				
Li Chi				

Who has the most money? _____
Who has the least money? _____

Canadian Money

$5.00 $2.00 $1.00   25¢   10¢   5¢   1¢

Draw the fewest coins and bills you could use to pay for each item.

$5.45 $0.89 $3.67 $7.92

Shawn has $9.64

Robert has $1.36 less money than Shawn.

How much money does Robert have? _____

Length

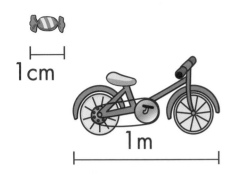

1cm

1m

1km

What units are the best to do these measurements?
Print km, m, or cm on the lines.

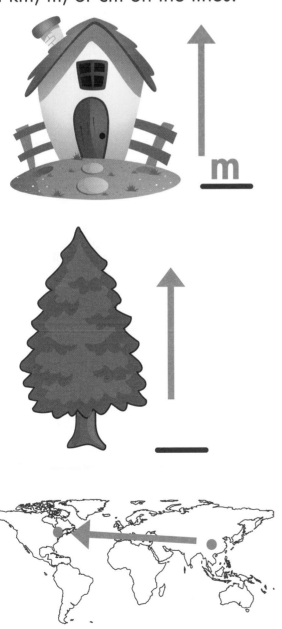

m

_____

_____

_____

_____

_____

_____

Length   Answer the questions using km, m , or cm.

How tall is the Prime Minister? About 2 _____ .

How long is your shoe? About 15 _____ .

How far is it from Calgary to Toronto? About 2 000 ____ .

How long is your dad's arm? About 1 ____ .

How tall is an apple? About 6 ____ .

Measure each line. Record the length in the box.
Don't forget to include the units.

14 cm

Length

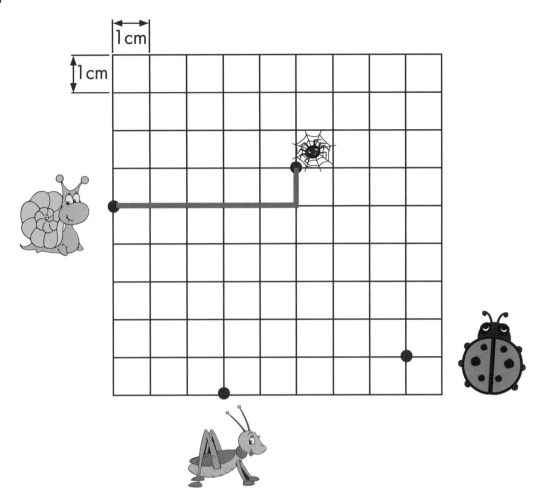

Using **green**, follow the lines to draw the route from the snail to the spider. How long is the route? ____6____ cm

Using **blue**, follow the lines to show the route from the spider to the cricket. How long is the route? _____ cm

Using **red**, follow the lines to draw the route from the ladybug to the snail. _____ cm

How far is it all together from the cricket to the lady bug, then to the spider, then to the snail, and back to the cricket? _____ cm
Draw the route **purple**.

Measurement

Time

When telling time, the short hand tells the hour and the long hand tells the minutes.

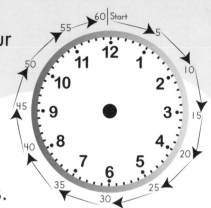

Skip count by 5 to count the minutes.
Start at 12.

Write the time shown to the nearest 5 minutes.

___4___ : __40__   ___10___ : __35__   ___8___ : __20__   ___10___ : __35__

_____ : _____   _____ : _____   _____ : _____   _____ : _____

__5__ minutes after __2__   _____ minutes before _____   _____ minutes before _____   _____ minutes after _____
                                                              _____ minutes after _____

Draw the hands to match the time on the digital clock.

| 9:05 | 12:50 | 2:10 | 5:35 |

Time Maze
Draw the hands on the clocks from start to end.

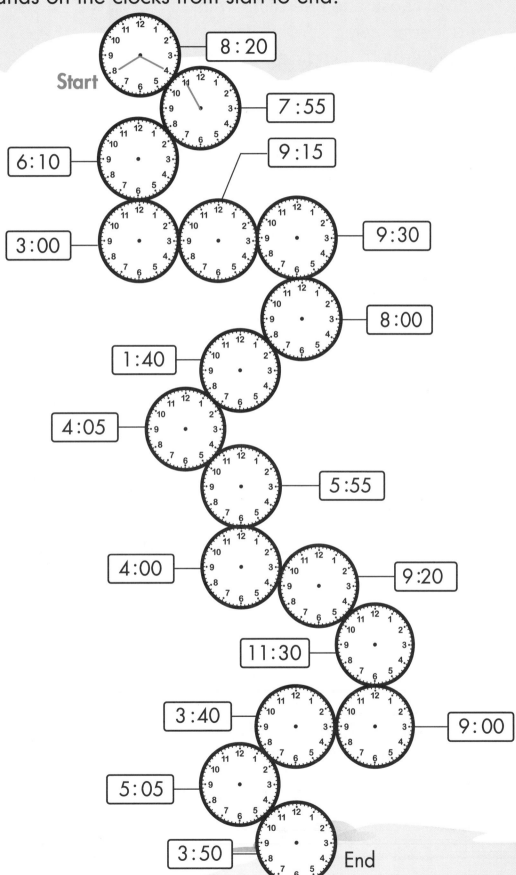

Temperature

We measure temperature with a thermometer. We tell the temperature using degrees Celcius (°C).

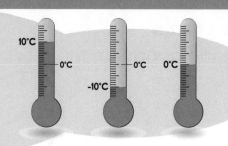

Write the temperature.

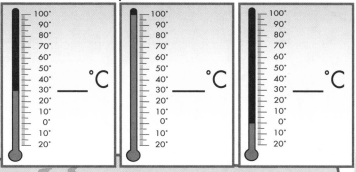

___°C ___°C ___°C

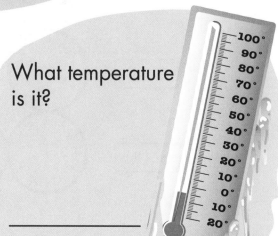

What temperature is it?

_____

HOT and COLD

Water turns to ice at 0°. It is cold.

 0°C

Water boils at 100°. It is hot.

 100°C

A nice warm day at the beach is 25°C. It is warm.

25°C

Circle the things that you need for this tempertaure.

Circle the correct temperature.

 100° C 25° C 0° C

 100° C 25° C 0° C

  100° C 25° C 0° C

Capacity

Capacity tells how much a container can hold. Millilitres (ml) and litres (L) are units for measuring capacity. One ml is smaller than an eraser. One L is about the amount in a water bottle.

What is the capacity of each container? Circle the answers. Some are done.

(less than 1L)
about 1L
more than 1L

less than 1L
about 1L
(more than 1L)

less than 1L
(about 1L)
more than 1L

less than 1L
about 1L
more than 1L

less than 1L
about 1L
more than 1L

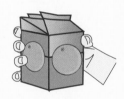

less than 1L
about 1L
more than 1L

Draw the amount of grape juice in each container.

Draw 2L.

3L
2L
1L

Draw 3L.

4L
3L
2L
1L

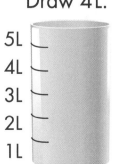

Draw 4L.

5L
4L
3L
2L
1L

Draw 8L.

9L
8L
7L
6L
5L
4L
3L
2L
1L

Capacity

What is the capacity of each container? Circle the answer.

about 50 L
more than 200 L

less than 1 L
about 10 L

less than 1L
about 10 L

Answer the questions.

3 L

12 L

How many pails full of water will fill the tub? _____

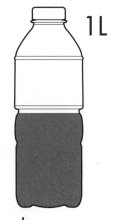

2 L

250ml

How many glasses can be filled from the full pitcher? _____

Hint: 1000 ml is 1 L
        2000 ml is 2 L

How much juice is in each container?
Use these words: a quarter of a litre, half a litre, three quarters of a litre

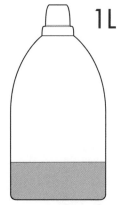

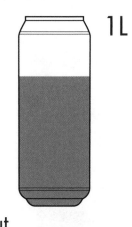

1L

1L

1L

about _____

about _____

about _____

Measurement

Mass

Mass tells the amount of substance in a thing.

Grams (g) and kilograms (kg) are units for measuring mass.

What is the mass of each object? Write it on the line. Two examples are done.

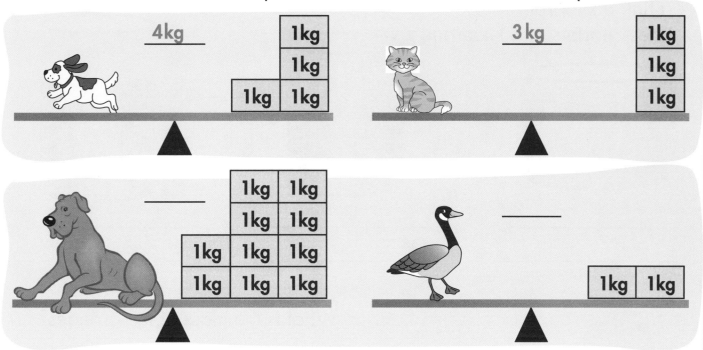

4 kg

3 kg

_____

_____

Draw the number of 1kg needed to balance the scales.

How many 1kg need to be added to the goose to equal the mass of the big dog?

_____

27

Mass

What is the mass of the grape jelly in each container?
Use these words:

    a quarter of a kilogram
    a half a kilogram
    three-quarters of a kilogram

_____   _____   _____

_____   _____   _____

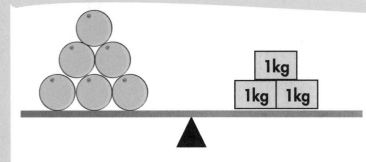

What is the mass of the oranges?

_____

What is the mass of one orange?

_____

What is the mass of 12 oranges?

_____

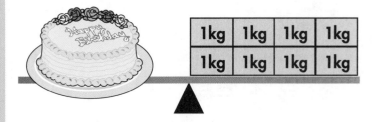

What is the mass of the cake? _____

What is the mass of half of the cake? _____

What is the mass of a quarter of the cake? _____

3-D Shapes

| cube | sphere | cylinder | cone | rectangular prism |

Colour the sphere shapes red.

Colour the cube shapes blue.

Colour the cylinder shapes green.

Colour the cone shapes orange.

Colour the rectangular prism shapes purple.

Cereal Shapes

29

Polygons

A **polygon** is a 2-D (flat) shape with 3 or more **sides** made of straight lines.
Here are 5 kinds of polygons.

 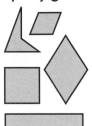 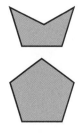 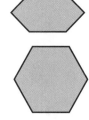 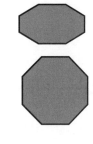

triangle	quadrilateral	pentagon	hexagon	octagon
• 3 sides	• 4 sides	• 5 sides	• 6 sides	• 8 sides

Print the name of each polygon on the line below the shape. Then colour it
to match the categories above.

quadrilateral
_____

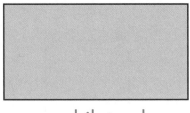

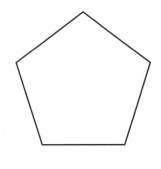

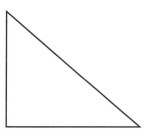

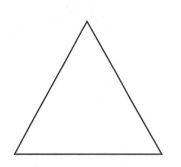

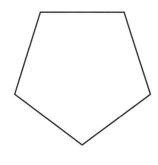

Polygons

A **polygon** has 3 or more straight **sides** or **edges**. The sides meet at the **vertices** (or **corners**). A single corner is called a **vertex.**

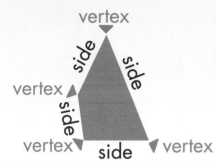

This polygon has 4 vertices and 4 sides.

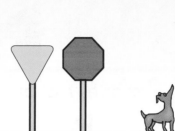

Fill in the number of sides and vertices for each polygon.

- __4__ sides
- __4__ vertices

- _____ sides
- _____ vertices

- _____ sides
- _____ vertices

- _____ sides
- _____ vertices

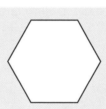

- _____ sides
- _____ vertices

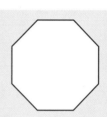

- _____ sides
- _____ vertices

Review:

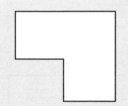 triangle: _____ sides
_____ vertices

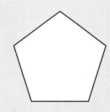 pentagon: _____ sides
_____ vertices

square: _____ sides
_____ vertices

 hexagon: _____ sides
_____ vertices

octagon: _____ sides
_____ vertices

rectangle: _____ sides
_____ vertices

Congruent Shapes

Shapes are **congruent** if they are the same size and the same shape. They can have different colours and patterns and can be facing different directions. These pairs are congruent.

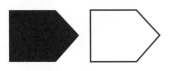  

Colour the pairs of shapes that are congruent.

A 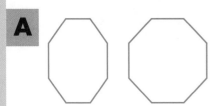 **B** 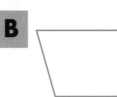   **C**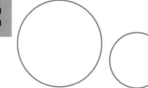

D 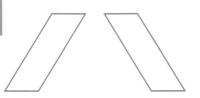 **E**  **F**

Colour the shape that is congruent to each shaded shape.

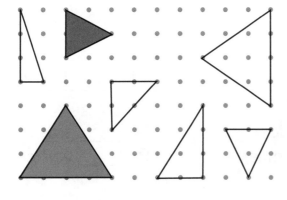 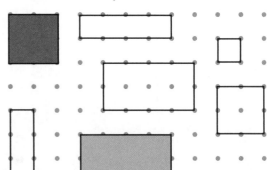

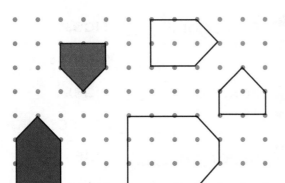 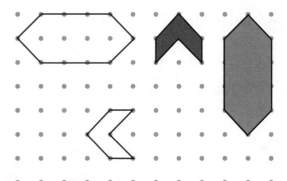

Congruent Shapes

Draw a shape that is congruent to each given figure. One is done.

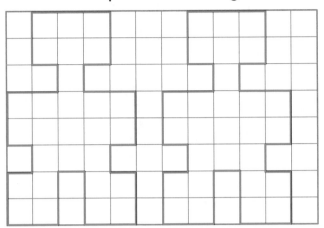 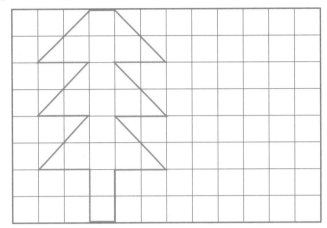

For each coloured shape find a congruent shape and colour it the same colour.

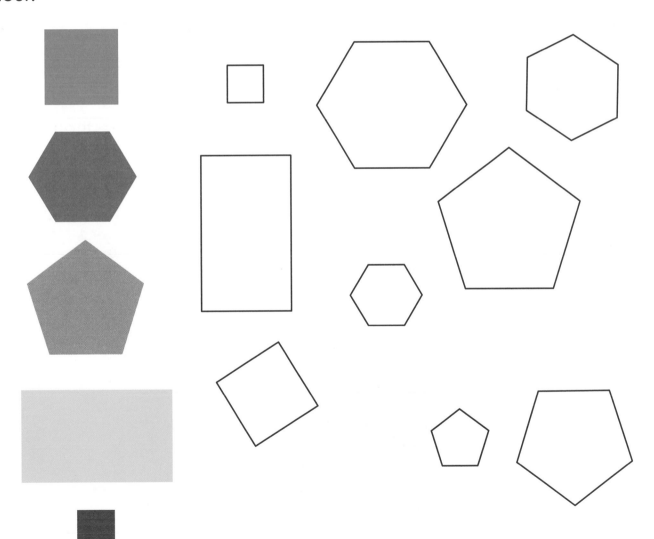

Symmetry

Some shapes have **lines of symmetry**. That means if the shape is cut in half each side is the mirror image of the other. You can check for symmetry by cutting the shape out and folding it. If the halves match exactly, the fold shows a line of symmetry. We say the shape is **symmetrical**.

The dotted line is the line of symmetry.

The dotted line is **not** the line of symmetry.

Circle the pictures where the dotted line shows the line of symmetry. Put an X on those where it does not.

  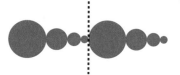 

Draw a line of symmetry on each shape. They each have more than one.

 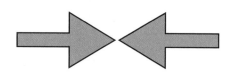 

Make the picture symmetrical by adding what is missing.

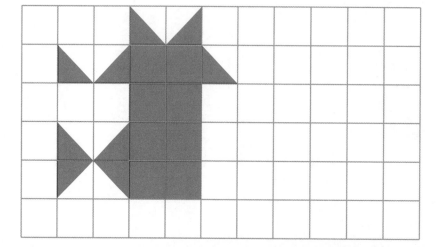

Prisms

A **prism** is a 3-D shape that has 2 **bases** that are the same, and **sides that are rectangles**. We identify a prism by its base shape.

Shape of bases: triangles
Prism name: triangular prism

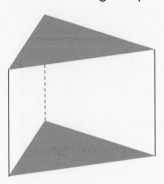

Shape of bases: rectangles
Prism name: rectangular prism

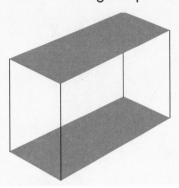

Shape of bases: pentagons
Prism name: pentagonal prism

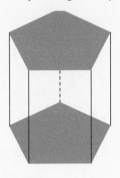

Identify these prisms by their base shape.

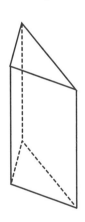

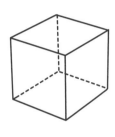

Shape of bases: _____

Prism name: _____

Shape of bases: _____

Prism name: _____

Shape of bases: _____

Prism name: _____

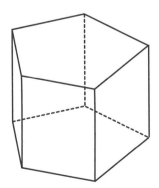

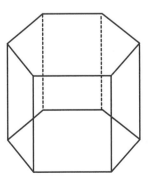

Shape of bases: _____

Prism name: _____

Shape of bases: _____

Prism name: _____

Geometry and Spatial Sense

Pyramids

Pyramids have **1 base** and **sides that are triangular** which meet at the top. Pyramids are identified by their bases.

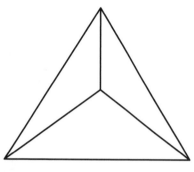

triangular pyramid

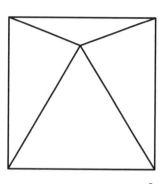

square pyramid

Colour the base of each pyramid.
Write the shape of the base on the line.

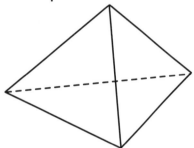

Shape of base: _____

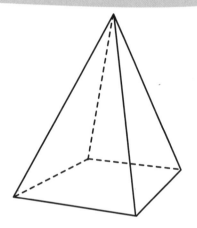

Shape of base: _____

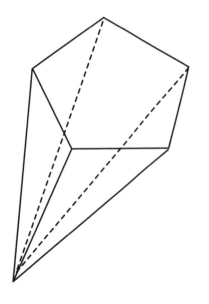

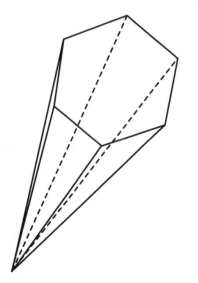

Shape of base: _____   Shape of base: _____

Prisms and Pyramids

Faces are the flat surfaces of a 3-D shape. Count the faces and edges on each shape. Record the numbers. Then circle the vertices. Count and record the numbers. Then colour the **prisms red** and the **pyramids blue**.

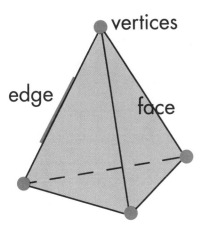

vertices

edge

face

____4____ faces
____6____ edges
____4____ vertices

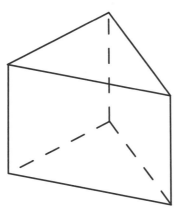

_____ faces
_____ edges
_____ vertices

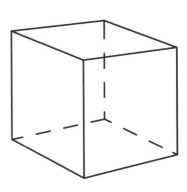

_____ faces
_____ edges
_____ vertices

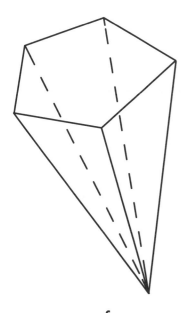

_____ faces
_____ edges
_____ vertices

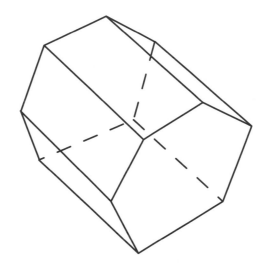

_____ faces
_____ edges
_____ vertices

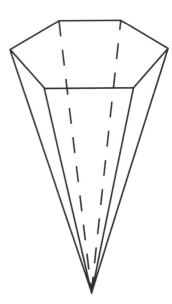

_____ faces
_____ edges
_____ vertices

Geometry and Spatial Sense

Location and Movement
Look at the grid map. Fill in the blanks.

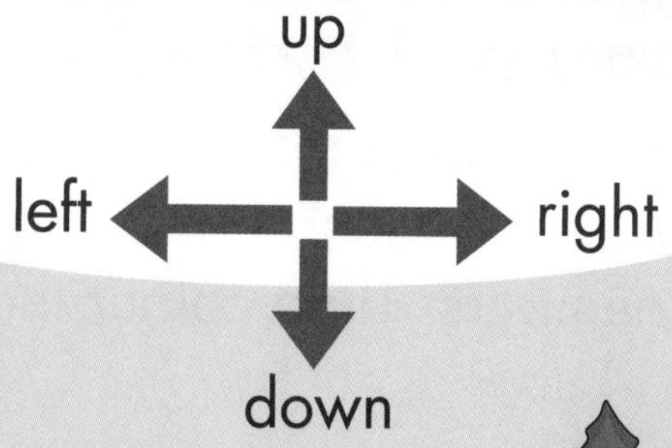

up

left ←→ right

down

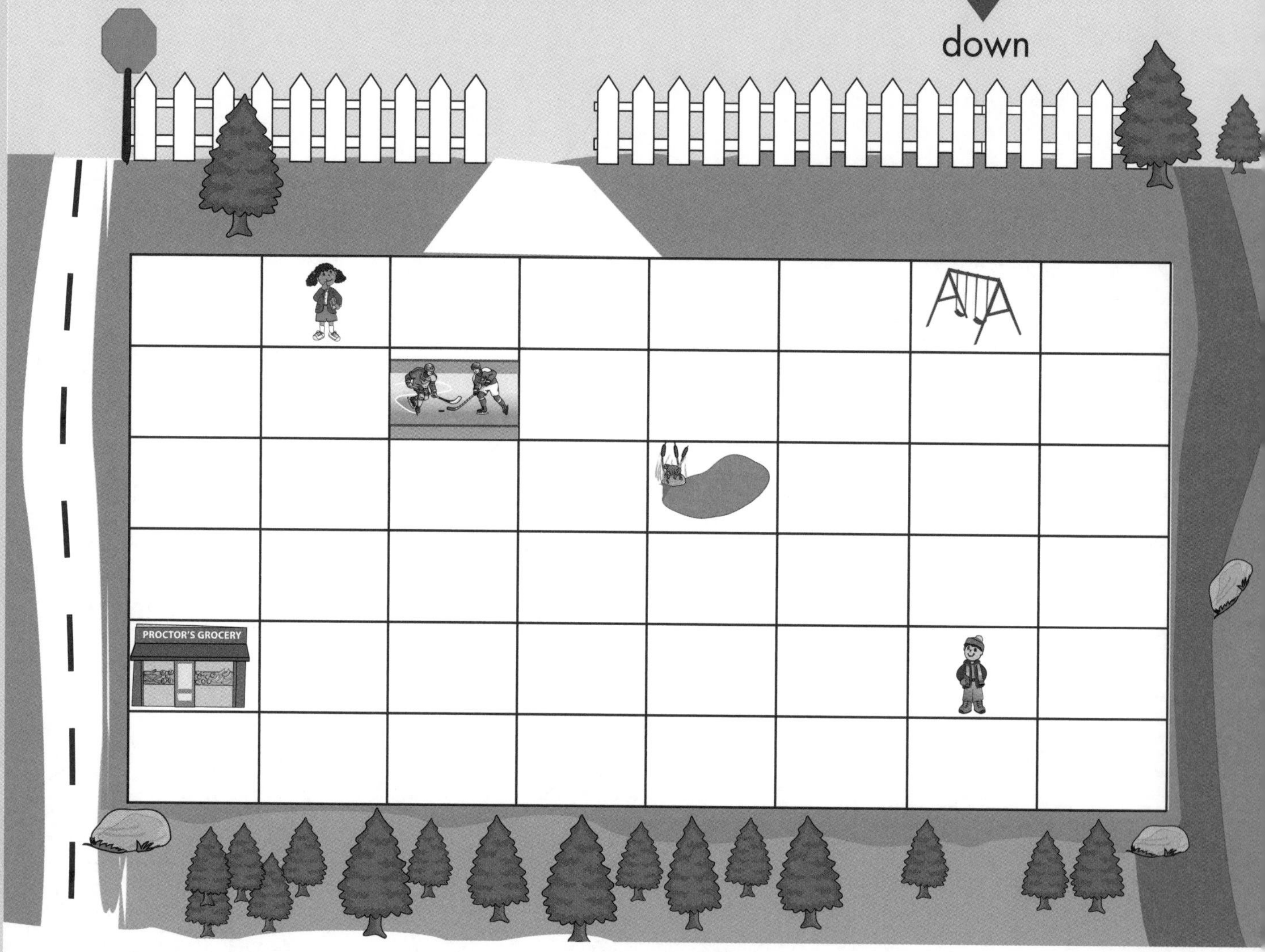

The skating rink is _____ squares to the left of the river.

The swing is _____ squares up from the trees.

The pond is _____ squares to the right of the road.

The store is _____ squares down from the fence.

Joe is _____ squares to the right of the store and _____ squares to the left of the river.

Jill is _____ squares to the right of the road and _____ squares to the left of the swing.

Location and Movement

Follow the instructions to move each item on the grid. Draw a line from square to square to the new location. Then draw the item in its new location.

 4 squares to the right and 1 square up.

 2 squares down and 5 squares left.

 2 squares to the right and 1 square down.

 3 squares to the left and 1 squares down.

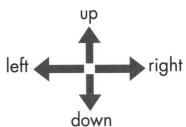

up

left ← → right

down

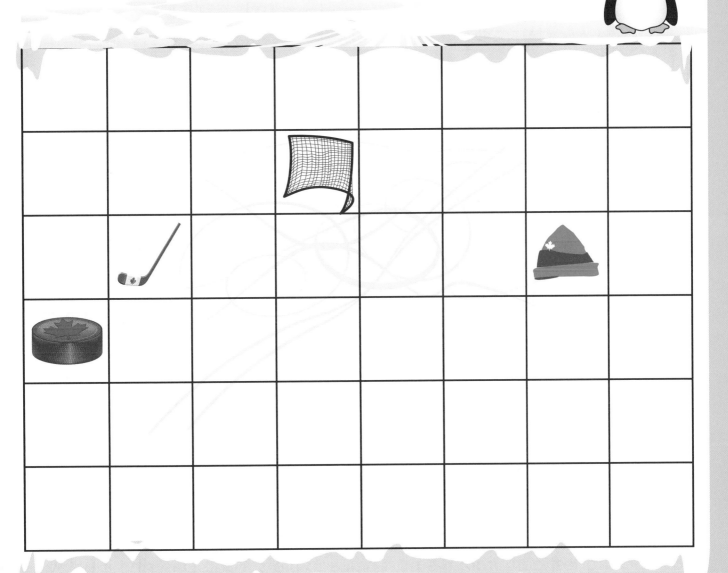

Geometry and Spatial Sense

Location and Movement
Look at the grid. Answer the questions.

Draw the shortest path from the grocery store to the post office.
Describe it below.

_____

Draw the shortest path from the park to the hospital. Describe it below.

_____

Draw the shortest path from the park to the bookstore. Describe it below.

_____

Draw the shortest path from the post office to the school. Describe it below.

_____

Patterning and Algebra

Patterns

Look at each pattern. Draw and colour the next three shapes.

Growing and Shrinking Patterns

A **growing** pattern gets larger every time.

A **shrinking** pattern gets smaller every time.

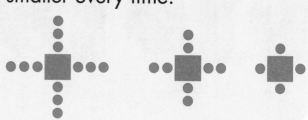

Fill in the blanks in the patterns.

 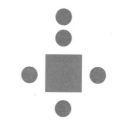

The pattern is _____growing_____.

The pattern is _____.

The pattern is _____.

2   4   ___   ___   10   ___   ___   ___

The pattern is _____.

55   50   45   ___   ___   30   ___   ___   ___

The pattern is _____.

Patterning Rules

Number patterns can be created by adding and/or subtracting numbers.

Create a number pattern by following the pattern rule.

Pattern rule: Add 4 each time.

0 ___4___ ___8___ _____ _____ _____ _____ _____

Add 3 each time.
15 _____ _____ _____ _____ _____ _____ _____

Subtract 4 each time.
64 _____ _____ _____ _____ _____ _____ _____

Subtract 5 each time.
50 _____ _____ _____ _____ _____ _____ _____

Follow the instructions to make patterns.

Start at 36. Make a number pattern that extends by adding 8 each time.

_____ _____ _____ _____ _____ _____ _____ _____

Start at 64. Make a number pattern that extends by subtracting 4 each time.

_____ _____ _____ _____ _____ _____ _____ _____

Fact Families

Look at each pair of number sentences. Find the missing number.

11 – 4 = 7
4 + _7_ = 11

13 + 16 = 29
29 – ___ = 16

16 + 23 = 39
___ – 23 = 16

14 – 7 = 7
7 + _7_ = 14

5 + 15 = 20
20 – ___ = 5

42 – 12 = 30
___ + 30 = 42

Beside each number sentence, write another number sentence in the same fact family. There are two possible answers.

31 + 6 = 37   _37 – 31 = 6   37 – 6 = 31_

5 + 6 = 11   _____

19 + 7 = 26   _____

12 + 5 = 17   _____

22 – 16 = 6   _____

8 + 7 = 15   _____

24 – 5 = 19   _____

22 – 18 = 4   _____

5 + 14 = 19   _____

9 + 5 = 14   _____

37 – 13 = 24   _____

35 – 28 = 7   _____

17 + 8 = 25
25 - 17 = 8
Math Patterning and Algebra

Fact Families Challenge: Equations

Remember that whatever is on one side of an = must be equal to what is on the other side. This is called an equation.

Try this challenge: Find the missing number in each equation. Use fact families to help.

Hint: First simplify the equation by solving the complete side of the equation.

Example:

$12 + 3 = \boxed{} - 6$

The complete side of the equation is 12 + 3. That adds up to 15, so

$15 = \boxed{} - 6$

If $\boxed{} - 6 = 15$, then by thinking of this fact family we know that

$15 + 6 = \boxed{}$

Now add the complete side of the equation to find the answer.

$15 + 6 = 21$

$\boxed{} = 21$

Simplify the equations below. Then solve them using fact families to help you. The first one gives hints.

$25 - 6 = \boxed{} + 14$

Simplify 25 – 6 and write the answer where the $\boxed{}$ is below.

$\boxed{} = \boxed{} + 14$

Now use the fact family help you.
Write the number again in the $\boxed{}$ below.

$\boxed{} - 14 = \boxed{}$

Now subtract to find the answer.

$\boxed{} =$

$\boxed{} - 6 = 15 + 15$

$\boxed{} - 6 = \boxed{}$

$\boxed{} + 6 = \boxed{}$

$\boxed{} =$

Graphs

Read the graph and answer the questions.

Thirty students in Ms. Kenny's class did a survey to find out what their favourite type of healthy snack was. This graph shows their data.

Favourite Snacks in Ms. Kenny's Class

fruit	
granola	
vegetables	
cheese and crackers	

Each picture represents _____ students.

1. If there are 30 students in Ms. Kenny's class, how many students does each piece of food represent? _____

   _____

2. What was the most popular snack? _____

3. What was the least popular snack? _____

4. How many people liked fruit best? _____

5. How many people liked granola best? _____

6. How many people liked vegetables best? _____

7. How many people liked cheese and crackers best? _____

8. What is your favourite type of healthy snack? _____

Graphs

The graph below is called a **bar graph**.
Read the graph and answer the questions.

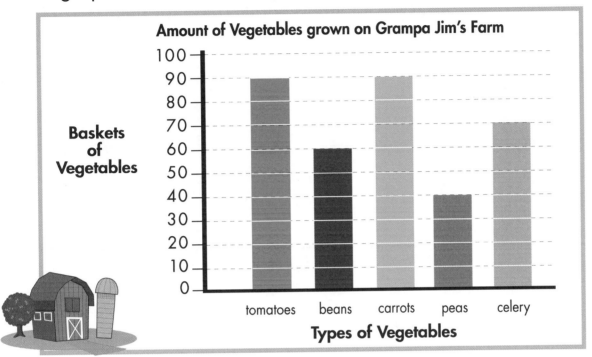

Amount of Vegetables grown on Grampa Jim's Farm

Baskets of Vegetables

Types of Vegetables

1. What does the graph tell us about? _____

_____

2. How many baskets of tomatoes does Grampa Jim grow? _____

_____

3. How many more beans than peas does he grow? _____

_____

4. What does Grampa Jim grow the most of? _____

_____

5. What does Grampa Jim grow the least of? _____

_____

6. How many types of vegetables does Grampa Jim grow? _____

_____

7. How many baskets of vegetables does Grampa Jim grow all together? _____

_____

Graphs

Mr. Milgram has 5 bakeries. He kept track of how long it took each bakery to sell 5 apple pies. Fill in the blanks and put the data in the graph. Then answer the questions. Look at the previous page for help.

Bakery	Number of Days to Sell 5 Pies
A	5
B	25
C	15
D	10
E	20

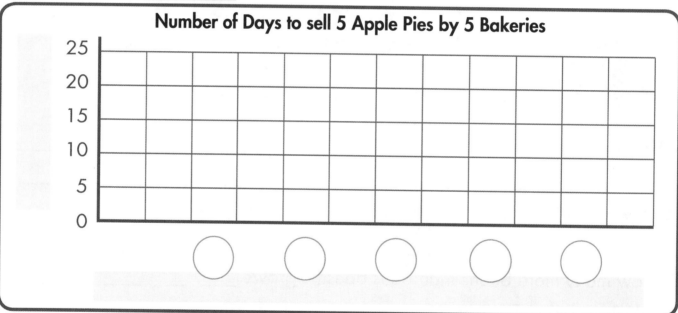

Number of Days to sell 5 Apple Pies by 5 Bakeries

What is the title of the graph?_____

How many days does each square represent? _____ days.

How many bakeries took more than 2 weeks to sell 5 apple pies?

_____bakeries.

Which bakery sold 5 apple pies in the shortest time? _____

Which bakery sold 5 apple pies in less than 2 weeks? _____

Graphs

Natasha is baking giant cookies for her school's bake sale. She is baking several different kinds of cookies.

Fill in the blanks and put the data in the horizontal bar graph.

Type of Cookie	Number
chocolate chip	24
oatmeal chocolate chip	18
sugar cookie	12
shortbread	12
gingerbread	18

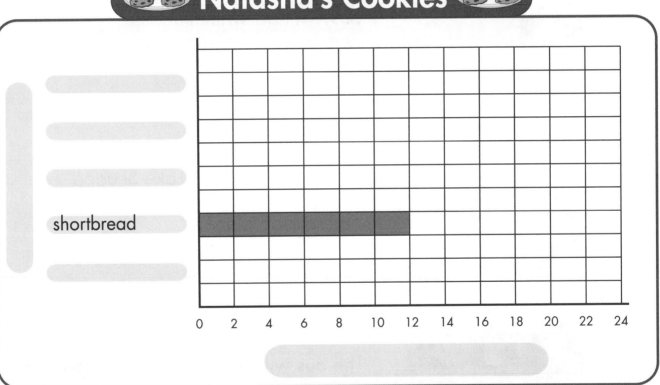

Natasha's Cookies

shortbread

0 2 4 6 8 10 12 14 16 18 20 22 24

How many different kinds of cookies is she baking? _____ kinds

How many different types of cookies have chocolate chips? _____ cookies

How many cookies has she made in all? _____ cookies

If each cookie cost $1, how much will be collected from selling

all the cookies? $_____

Probability

How likely is each event?
Print the answer on the line.
Use the words here: **impossible**, **unlikely**, **likely**, or **certain**.

The bee will return to the hive to make honey.

_____

Susy will go swimming.

_____

Jimmy will canoe in Lake Scugog.

_____

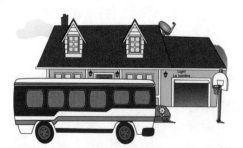

The bus will fit in my single car garage.

_____

The fire truck will put out the fire.

_____

Probability is the chance that a certain outcome will occur.

If you flip a coin the probability that it will land on heads is 1 for every 2 times thrown.

Look at the blocks in the box. If you take one block out 20 times in a row. without looking, how many times will you take out each type of block? Circle the best prediction.

 2 times and 18 times

15 times and 5 times

 10 times and 10 times

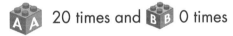 20 times and 0 times

Look at the marbles in a bowl. If you take one marble out 40 times in a row without looking, how many times will you take out each colour marble? Circle the best prediction.

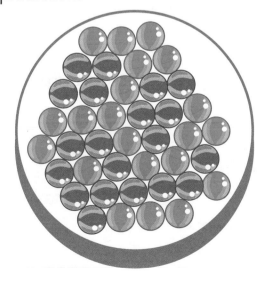

🔵 40 times and ⚫ 0 times

🔵 18 times and ⚫ 22 times

🔵 7 times and ⚫ 33 times

🔵 30 times and ⚫ 10 times

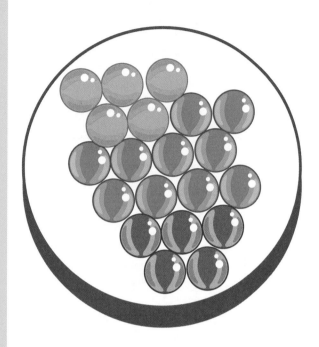

Take one marble from the bowl. What are the possible outcomes?

_____

Are the chances of taking a or a the same? _____

_____

Are the chances of taking a or a the same? _____

_____

If you take out a marble 40 times without looking, how many times will you take out each colour marble? Put your prediction on the line.

_____ times

_____ times

_____ times

Spin the arrow once. What are the possible outcomes?

_____

If you spin the arrow 50 times without looking, how many times do you predict it will land on each colour?

Green _____ times

Blue _____ times

Yellow _____ times

Red _____ time

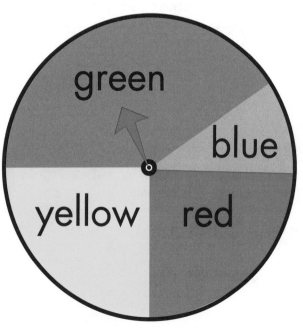

Data Management and Probability

Think about it:

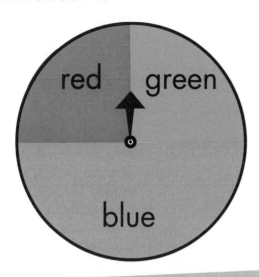

What is the probability that the spinner will land on yellow? **Impossible**

Is it more likely for the spinner to land on red or green? **It is equally likely because the red and green section are equal size.**

Is it impossible, unlikely, likely, or certain that the spinner will land on blue? **It is likely because blue is the largest section.**

Read the descriptions and colour the spinners to match.

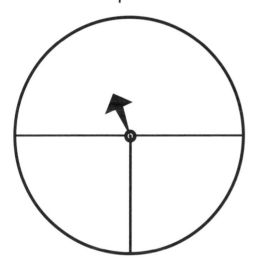

It is equally likely for the spinner to land on purple or green.

It is likely for the spinner to land on red.

It is impossible for the spinner to land on blue.

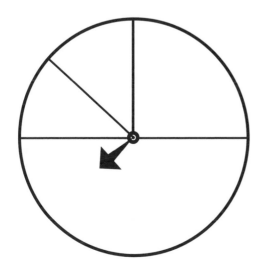

It is equally likely for the spinner to land on yellow or green.

It is more likely for the spinner to land on red than purple.

Think about it: Circle the words to finish the sentences:

Example:

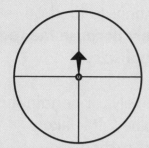

Each outcome is **equally likely**.

The sections are **congruent**.

The spinner is **fair**.

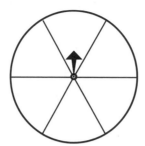

Each outcome
    is equally likely.
    is not equally likely.
These sections are
    congruent incongruent
The spinner is **fair unfair**.

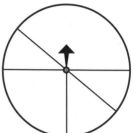

Each outcome
    is equally likely.
    is not equally likely.
These sections are
    congruent incongruent
The spinner is **fair unfair**.

Circle the correct word to complete the sentences.
This spinner has 8 **congruent**
                   incongruent sections.

Answer the questions.

Out of 8 sections, how many sections say "win"? _____

Out of 8 sections, how many sections say "lose"? _____

Out of 8 sections, how many sections say "try again"? _____

What is the probability of each outcome?

Win   ____ in ____

Lose   ____ in ____

Try again   ____ in ____

Is the spinner fair?   Yes   No

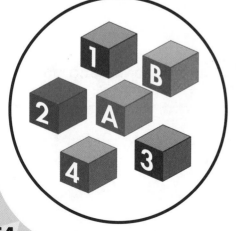

If you take one block out without looking, what is the probability of each outcome?

A   ____ in ____

A number   ____ in ____

A letter   ____ in ____

An even number   ____ in ____

Venn Diagrams

A Venn diagram represents sets using circles. Where the circles intersect, the items are included in both circles.

Children Who Play Soccer   Children Who Practice Karate

Nine children were surveyed to find out if they played soccer, practiced karate, or both. Look at the Venn diagram to answer the following questions.

How many children play soccer? _____

How many children practice karate? _____

How many children play soccer and practice karate? _____

What activity do Amir and Kate have in common? _____

How many children play soccer but do not practice karate?_____

How many children practice karate but do not play soccer? _____

Solutions

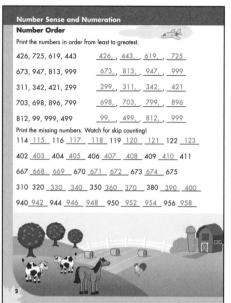

Number Sense and Numeration
Number Order

Print the numbers in order from least to greatest.

426, 725, 619, 443   <u>426,</u> <u>443,</u> <u>619,</u> <u>725</u>

673, 947, 813, 999   <u>673,</u> <u>813,</u> <u>947,</u> <u>999</u>

311, 342, 421, 299   <u>299,</u> <u>311,</u> <u>342,</u> <u>421</u>

703, 698, 896, 799   <u>698,</u> <u>703,</u> <u>799,</u> <u>896</u>

812, 99, 999, 499   <u>99,</u> <u>499,</u> <u>812,</u> <u>999</u>

Print the missing numbers. Watch for skip counting!

114 <u>115</u> 116 <u>117</u> <u>118</u> 119 <u>120</u> <u>121</u> 122 <u>123</u>

402 <u>403</u> 404 <u>405</u> 406 <u>407</u> <u>408</u> 409 <u>410</u> 411

667 <u>668</u> <u>669</u> 670 <u>671</u> <u>672</u> 673 <u>674</u> 675

310 320 <u>330</u> <u>340</u> 350 <u>360</u> <u>370</u> 380 <u>390</u> <u>400</u>

940 <u>942</u> 944 <u>946</u> 948 950 <u>952</u> <u>954</u> 956 <u>958</u>

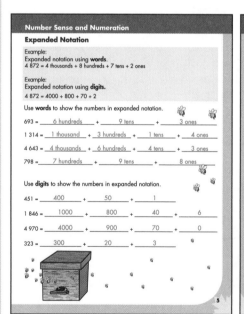

Page 2

Number Sense and Numeration
Thousands, Hundreds, Tens, and Ones
Example:

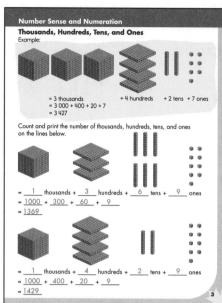

= 3 thousands   + 4 hundreds   + 2 tens + 7 ones
= 3 000 + 400 + 20 + 7
= 3 427

Count and print the number of thousands, hundreds, tens, and ones on the lines below.

= <u>1</u> thousands + <u>3</u> hundreds + <u>6</u> tens + <u>9</u> ones
= <u>1000</u> + <u>300</u> + <u>60</u> + <u>9</u>
= <u>1369</u>

= <u>1</u> thousands + <u>4</u> hundreds + <u>2</u> tens + <u>9</u> ones
= <u>1000</u> + <u>400</u> + <u>20</u> + <u>9</u>
= <u>1429</u>

Page 3

Number Sense and Numeration
Thousands, Hundreds, Tens, and Ones

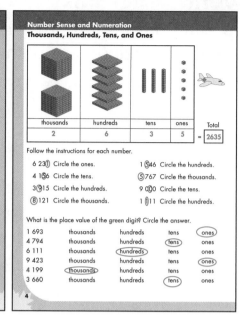

thousands	hundreds	tens	ones	Total
2	6	3	5	= 2635

Follow the instructions for each number.

6 23(1) Circle the ones.   1 (5)46 Circle the hundreds.

4 1(5)6 Circle the tens.   (5)767 Circle the thousands.

3(9)15 Circle the hundreds.   9 0(0)0 Circle the tens.

(8)121 Circle the thousands.   1 (0)11 Circle the hundreds.

What is the place value of the green digit? Circle the answer.

1 693	thousands	hundreds	tens	(ones)
4 794	thousands	hundreds	(tens)	ones
6 111	thousands	(hundreds)	tens	ones
9 423	thousands	hundreds	tens	(ones)
4 199	(thousands)	hundreds	tens	ones
3 660	thousands	hundreds	(tens)	ones

Page 4

Number Sense and Numeration
Expanded Notation

Example:
Expanded notation using **words**.
4 872 = 4 thousands + 8 hundreds + 7 tens + 2 ones

Example:
Expanded notation using **digits**.
4 872 = 4000 + 800 + 70 + 2

Use **words** to show the numbers in expanded notation.

693 = <u>6 hundreds</u> + <u>9 tens</u> + <u>3 ones</u>

1 314 = <u>1 thousand</u> + <u>3 hundreds</u> + <u>1 tens</u> + <u>4 ones</u>

4 643 = <u>4 thousands</u> + <u>6 hundreds</u> + <u>4 tens</u> + <u>3 ones</u>

798 = <u>7 hundreds</u> + <u>9 tens</u> + <u>8 ones</u>

Use **digits** to show the numbers in expanded notation.

451 = <u>400</u> + <u>50</u> + <u>1</u>

1 846 = <u>1000</u> + <u>800</u> + <u>40</u> + 6

4 970 = <u>4000</u> + <u>900</u> + <u>70</u> + <u>0</u>

323 = <u>300</u> + <u>20</u> + <u>3</u>

Page 5

Number Sense and Numeration
Addition Without Regrouping

When we add, we find the sum. First we add the ones, then the tens, and then the hundreds.

Add the ones: Next add the tens: Next add the hundreds:

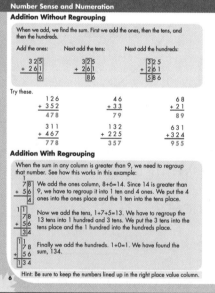

Try these.

```
  126          46          68
+ 352        + 33        + 21
  478          79          89

  311         132         631
+ 467        + 225       +324
  778          357         955
```

Addition With Regrouping

When the sum in any column is greater than 9, we need to regroup that number. See how this works in this example:

We add the ones column, 8+6=14. Since 14 is greater than 9, we have to regroup it into 1 ten and 4 ones. We put the 4 ones into the ones place and the 1 ten into the tens place.

Now we add the tens, 1+7+5=13. We have to regroup the 13 tens into 1 hundred and 3 tens. We put the 3 tens into the tens place and the 1 hundred into the hundreds place.

Finally we add the hundreds. 1+0=1. We have found the sum, 134.

Hint: Be sure to keep the numbers lined up in the right place value column.

Page 6

Number Sense and Numeration
Add:

```
   25       26       156       816
 +36      +48       +27      +159
   61       74       183       975

   78       71       321       267
 +15      +19       +88      +247
   93       90       409       514

   43       84       477       699
 +48      +17      +183      +128
   91      101       660       827

   75       37       765       575
 +25      +57      +476      +426
  100       94      1241      1001
```

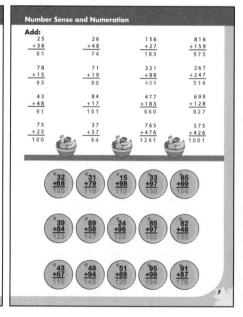

Page 7

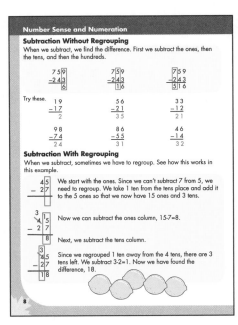

Number Sense and Numeration

Subtraction Without Regrouping

When we subtract, we find the difference. First we subtract the ones, then the tens, and then the hundreds.

```
7 5 9      7 5 9      7 5 9
-2 4 3     -2 4 3     -2 4 3
      6        1 6      5 1 6
```

Try these.

```
 1 9      5 6      3 3
-1 7     -2 1     -1 2
   2      3 5      2 1

 9 8      8 6      4 6
-7 4     -5 5     -1 4
 2 4      3 1      3 2
```

Subtraction With Regrouping

When we subtract, sometimes we have to regroup. See how this works in this example.

```
4 5
-2 7
```
We start with the ones. Since we can't subtract 7 from 5, we need to regroup. We take 1 ten from the tens place and add it to the 5 ones so that we now have 15 ones and 3 tens.

```
3
4 15
-2 7
    8
```
Now we can subtract the ones column, 15-7=8.

Next, we subtract the tens column.

```
3
4 15
-2 7
1 8
```
Since we regrouped 1 ten away from the 4 tens, there are 3 tens left. We subtract 3-2=1. Now we have found the difference, 18.

Page 8

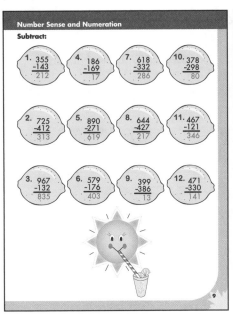

Number Sense and Numeration

Subtract:

1. 355 −143 = 212
4. 186 −169 = 17
7. 618 −332 = 286
10. 378 −298 = 80

2. 725 −412 = 313
5. 890 −271 = 619
8. 644 −427 = 217
11. 467 −121 = 346

3. 967 −132 = 835
6. 579 −176 = 403
9. 399 −386 = 13
12. 471 −330 = 141

Page 9

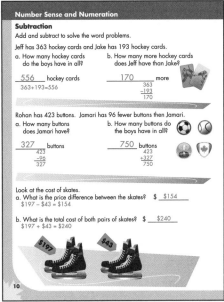

Number Sense and Numeration

Subtraction

Add and subtract to solve the word problems.

Jeff has 363 hockey cards and Jake has 193 hockey cards.

a. How many hockey cards do the boys have in all?

__556__ hockey cards
363+193=556

b. How many more hockey cards does Jeff have than Jake?

__170__ more
363 −193 = 170

Rohan has 423 buttons. Jamari has 96 fewer buttons then Jamari.

a. How many buttons does Jamari have?

__327__ buttons
423 −96 = 327

b. How many buttons do the boys have in all?

__750__ buttons
423 +327 = 750

Look at the cost of skates.

a. What is the price difference between the skates? $ __$154__
$197 − $43 = $154

b. What is the total cost of both pairs of skates? $ __$240__
$197 + $43 = $240

Page 10

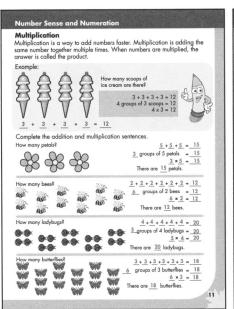

Number Sense and Numeration

Multiplication

Multiplication is a way to add numbers faster. Multiplication is adding the same number together multiple times. When numbers are multiplied, the answer is called the product.

Example:

How many scoops of ice cream are there?

3 + 3 + 3 + 3 = 12
4 groups of 3 scoops = 12
4 x 3 = 12

3 + 3 + 3 + 3 = 12

Complete the addition and multiplication sentences.

How many petals?

5 + 5 + 5 = 15
3 groups of 5 petals = 15
3 x 5 = 15
There are 15 petals.

How many bees?

2 + 2 + 2 + 2 + 2 + 2 = 12
6 groups of 2 bees = 12
6 x 2 = 12
There are 12 bees.

How many ladybugs?

4 + 4 + 4 + 4 + 4 = 20
5 groups of 4 ladybugs = 20
5 x 4 = 20
There are 20 ladybugs.

How many butterflies?

3 + 3 + 3 + 3 + 3 + 3 = 18
6 groups of 3 butterflies = 18
6 x 3 = 18
There are 18 butterflies.

Page 11

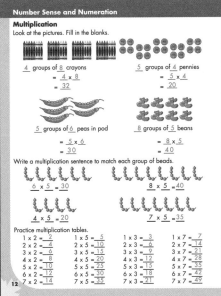

Number Sense and Numeration

Multiplication

Look at the pictures. Fill in the blanks.

4 groups of 8 crayons
= 4 x 8
= 32

5 groups of 4 pennies
= 5 x 4
= 20

5 groups of 6 peas in pod
= 5 x 6
= 30

8 groups of 5 beans
= 8 x 5
= 40

Write a multiplication sentence to match each group of beads.

6 x 5 = 30

8 x 5 = 40

4 x 5 = 20

7 x 5 = 35

Practice multiplication tables.

1 x 2 = 2   1 x 5 = 5   1 x 3 = 3   1 x 7 = 7
2 x 2 = 4   2 x 5 = 10   2 x 3 = 6   2 x 7 = 14
3 x 2 = 6   3 x 5 = 15   3 x 3 = 9   3 x 7 = 21
4 x 2 = 8   4 x 5 = 20   4 x 3 = 12   4 x 7 = 28
5 x 2 = 10   5 x 5 = 25   5 x 3 = 15   5 x 7 = 35
6 x 2 = 12   6 x 5 = 30   6 x 3 = 18   6 x 7 = 42
7 x 2 = 14   7 x 5 = 35   7 x 3 = 21   7 x 7 = 49

Page 12

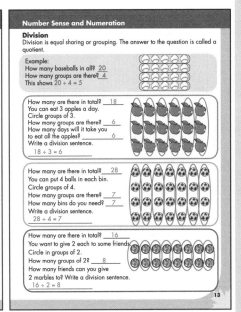

Number Sense and Numeration

Division

Division is equal sharing or grouping. The answer to the question is called a quotient.

Example:
How many baseballs in all? 20
How many groups are there? 4
This shows 20 ÷ 4 = 5

How many are there in total? 18
You can eat 3 apples a day.
Circle groups of 3.
How many groups are there? 6
How many days will it take you to eat all the apples? 6
Write a division sentence.
18 ÷ 3 = 6

How many are there in total? 28
You can put 4 balls in each bin.
Circle groups of 4.
How many groups are there? 7
How many bins do you need? 7
Write a division sentence.
28 ÷ 4 = 7

How many are there in total? 16
You want to give 2 each to some friends.
Circle in groups of 2.
How many groups of 2? 8
How many friends can you give 2 marbles to? Write a division sentence.
16 ÷ 2 = 8

Page 13

Solutions

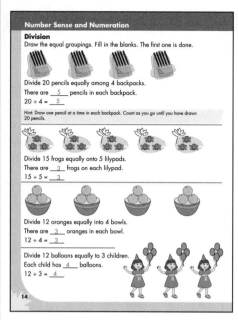

Number Sense and Numeration

Division

Draw the equal groupings. Fill in the blanks. The first one is done.

Divide 20 pencils equally among 4 backpacks.

There are ___5___ pencils in each backpack.

20 ÷ 4 = ___5___

Hint: Draw one pencil at a time in each backpack. Count as you go until you have drawn 20 pencils.

Divide 15 frogs equally onto 5 lilypads.

There are ___3___ frogs on each lilypad.

15 ÷ 5 = ___3___

Divide 12 oranges equally into 4 bowls.

There are ___3___ oranges in each bowl.

12 ÷ 4 = ___3___

Divide 12 balloons equally to 3 children.

Each child has ___4___ balloons.

12 ÷ 3 = ___4___

Page 14

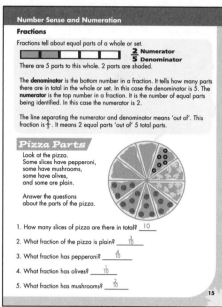

Number Sense and Numeration

Fractions

Fractions tell about equal parts of a whole or set.

$\frac{2}{5}$ Numerator / Denominator

There are 5 parts to this whole. 2 parts are shaded.

The **denominator** is the bottom number in a fraction. It tells how many parts there are in total in the whole or set. In this case the denominator is 5. The **numerator** is the top number in a fraction. It is the number of equal parts being identified. In this case the numerator is 2.

The line separating the numerator and denominator means 'out of'. This fraction is $\frac{2}{5}$. It means 2 equal parts 'out of' 5 total parts.

Pizza Parts

Look at the pizza. Some slices have pepperoni, some have mushrooms, some have olives, and some are plain.

Answer the questions about the parts of the pizza.

1. How many slices of pizza are there in total? ___10___

2. What fraction of the pizza is plain? ___$\frac{3}{10}$___

3. What fraction has pepperoni? ___$\frac{4}{10}$___

4. What fraction has olives? ___$\frac{1}{10}$___

5. What fraction has mushrooms? ___$\frac{2}{10}$___

Page 15

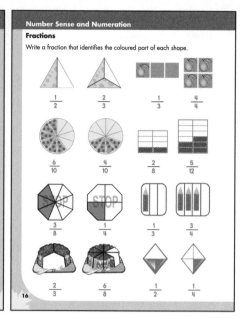

Number Sense and Numeration

Fractions

Write a fraction that identifies the coloured part of each shape.

$\frac{1}{2}$ $\frac{2}{3}$ $\frac{1}{3}$ $\frac{4}{4}$

$\frac{6}{10}$ $\frac{4}{10}$ $\frac{2}{8}$ $\frac{5}{12}$

$\frac{3}{8}$ $\frac{1}{4}$ $\frac{1}{3}$ $\frac{3}{4}$

$\frac{2}{3}$ $\frac{6}{8}$ $\frac{1}{2}$ $\frac{1}{4}$

Page 16

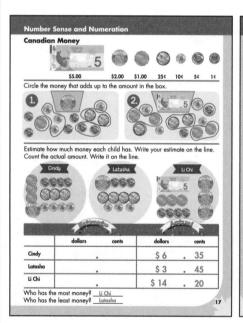

Number Sense and Numeration

Canadian Money

$5.00 $2.00 $1.00   25¢   10¢   5¢   1¢

Circle the money that adds up to the amount in the box.

1.   2.

Estimate how much money each child has. Write your estimate on the line. Count the actual amount. Write it on the line.

Cindy   Latasha   Li Chi

	dollars	cents	dollars	cents
Cindy	.		$ 6	35
Latasha	.		$ 3	45
Li Chi	.		$ 14	20

Who has the most money? ___Li Chi___

Who has the least money? ___Latasha___

Page 17

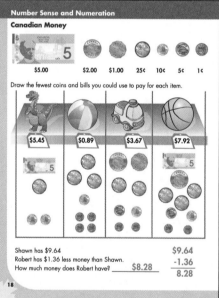

Number Sense and Numeration

Canadian Money

$5.00 $2.00 $1.00   25¢   10¢   5¢   1¢

Draw the fewest coins and bills you could use to pay for each item.

$5.45 $0.89 $3.67 $7.92

Shawn has $9.64

Robert has $1.36 less money than Shawn.

How much money does Robert have? ___$8.28___

```
  9.64
- 1.36
  8.28
```

Page 18

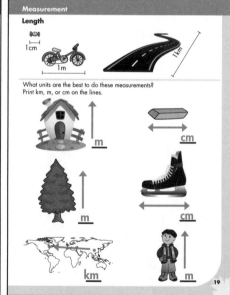

Measurement

Length

1cm

1m   1km

What units are the best to do these measurements? Print km, m, or cm on the lines.

___m___   ___cm___

___m___   ___cm___

___km___   ___m___

Page 19

Solutions

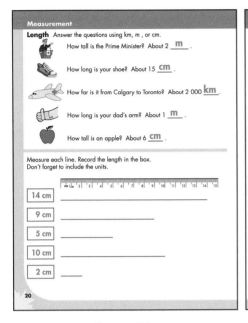

Page 20

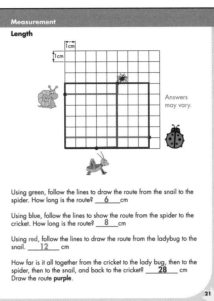

Page 21

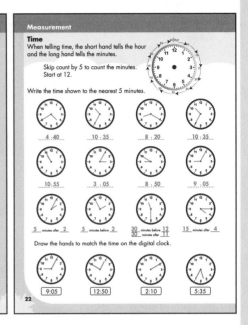

Page 22

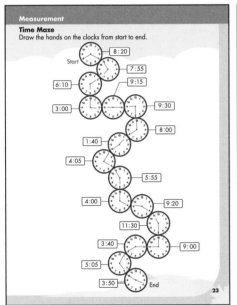

Page 23

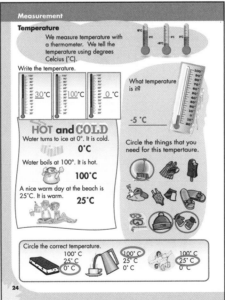

Page 24

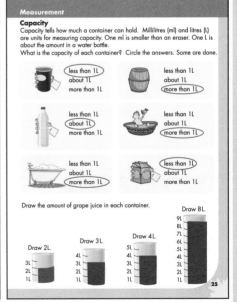

Page 25

Solutions

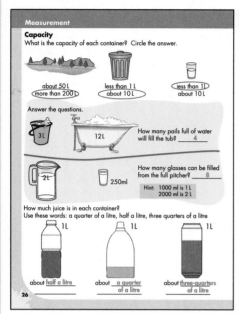

Page 26

Page 27

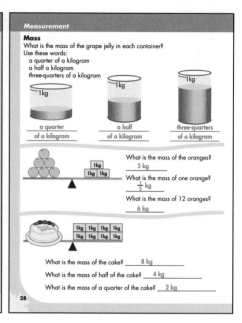

Page 28

Page 29

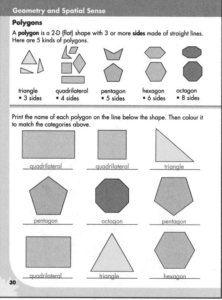

Page 30

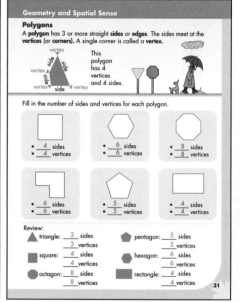

Page 31

Solutions

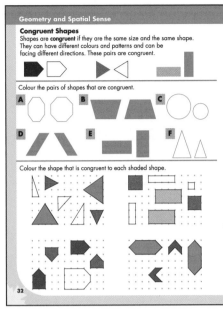

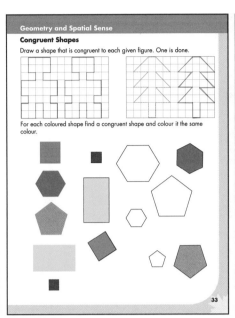

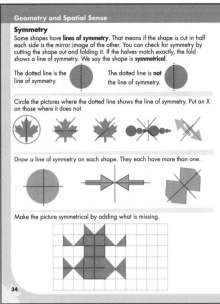

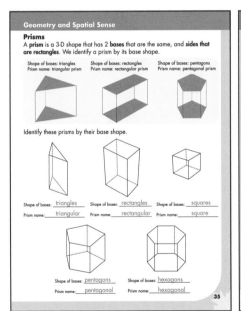

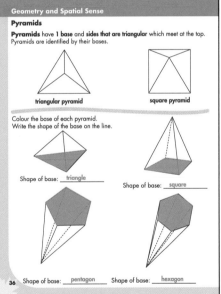

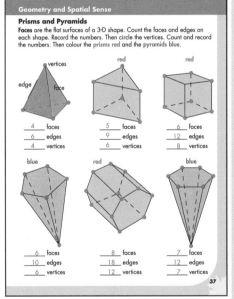

Solutions

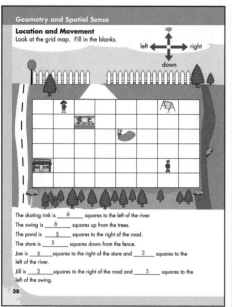

Page 38

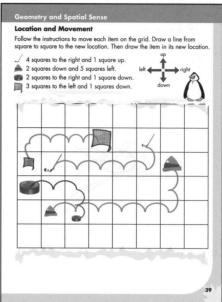

Page 39

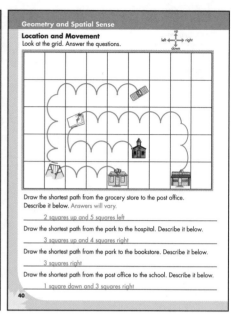

Page 40

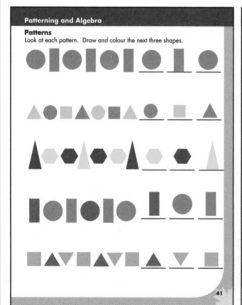

Page 41

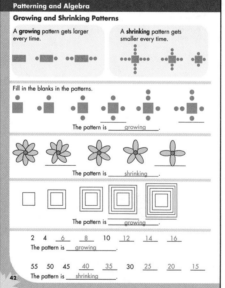

Page 42

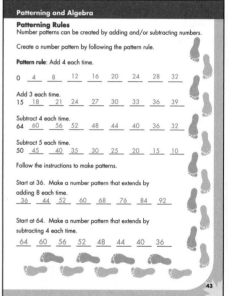

Page 43

Solutions

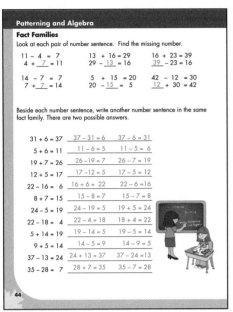

Patterning and Algebra
Fact Families
Look at each pair of number sentence. Find the missing number.

$11 - 4 = 7$	$13 + 16 = 29$	$16 + 23 = 39$
$4 + \underline{7} = 11$	$29 - \underline{13} = 16$	$\underline{39} - 23 = 16$
$14 - 7 = 7$	$5 + 15 = 20$	$42 - 12 = 30$
$7 + \underline{7} = 14$	$20 - \underline{15} = 5$	$\underline{12} + 30 = 42$

Beside each number sentence, write another number sentence in the same fact family. There are two possible answers.

$31 + 6 = 37$	$37 - 31 = 6$	$37 - 6 = 31$
$5 + 6 = 11$	$11 - 6 = 5$	$11 - 5 = 6$
$19 + 7 = 26$	$26 - 19 = 7$	$26 - 7 = 19$
$12 + 5 = 17$	$17 - 12 = 5$	$17 - 5 = 12$
$22 - 16 = 6$	$16 + 6 = 22$	$22 - 6 = 16$
$8 + 7 = 15$	$15 - 8 = 7$	$15 - 7 = 8$
$24 - 5 = 19$	$24 - 19 = 5$	$19 + 5 = 24$
$22 - 18 = 4$	$22 - 4 = 18$	$18 + 4 = 22$
$5 + 14 = 19$	$19 - 14 = 5$	$19 - 5 = 14$
$9 + 5 = 14$	$14 - 5 = 9$	$14 - 9 = 5$
$37 - 13 = 24$	$24 + 13 = 37$	$37 - 24 = 13$
$35 - 28 = 7$	$28 + 7 = 35$	$35 - 7 = 28$

44

Page 44

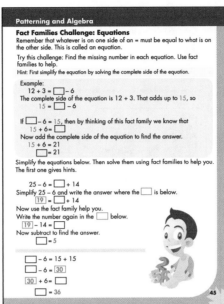

Patterning and Algebra
Fact Families Challenge: Equations
Remember that whatever is on one side of an = must be equal to what is on the other side. This is called an equation.

Try this challenge: Find the missing number in each equation. Use fact families to help.
Hint: First simplify the equation by solving the complete side of the equation.

Example:
$12 + 3 = \square - 6$
The complete side of the equation is $12 + 3$. That adds up to 15, so
$15 = \square - 6$

If $\square - 6 = \underline{15}$, then by thinking of this fact family we know that
$15 + 6 = \square$
Now add the complete side of the equation to find the answer.
$15 + 6 = 21$
$\square = 21$

Simplify the equations below. Then solve them using fact families to help you. The first one gives hints.

$25 - 6 = \square + 14$
Simplify $25 - 6$ and write the answer where the $\square$ is below.
$\boxed{19} = \square + 14$
Now use the fact family help you.
Write the number again in the $\square$ below.
$\boxed{19} - 14 = \square$
Now subtract to find the answer.
$\square = 5$

$\square - 6 = 15 + 15$
$\square - 6 = \boxed{30}$
$\boxed{30} + 6 = \square$
$\square = 36$

45

Page 45

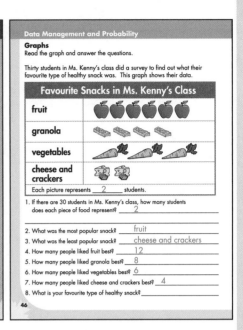

Data Management and Probability
Graphs
Read the graph and answer the questions.

Thirty students in Ms. Kenny's class did a survey to find out what their favourite type of healthy snack was. This graph shows their data.

Favourite Snacks in Ms. Kenny's Class

fruit	🍎🍎🍎🍎🍎🍎
granola	
vegetables	
cheese and crackers	

Each picture represents __2__ students.

1. If there are 30 students in Ms. Kenny's class, how many students does each piece of food represent? __2__

2. What was the most popular snack? __fruit__
3. What was the least popular snack? __cheese and crackers__
4. How many people liked fruit best? __12__
5. How many people liked granola best? __8__
6. How many people liked vegetables best? __6__
7. How many people liked cheese and crackers best? __4__
8. What is your favourite type of healthy snack? _____

46

Page 46

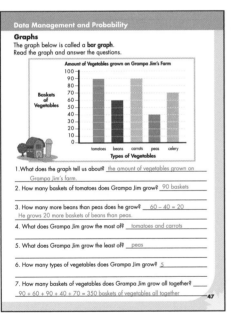

Data Management and Probability
Graphs
The graph below is called a **bar graph**.
Read the graph and answer the questions.

Amount of Vegetables grown on Grampa Jim's Farm

1. What does the graph tell us about? __the amount of vegetables grown on Grampa Jim's farm.__

2. How many baskets of tomatoes does Grampa Jim grow? __90 baskets__

3. How many more beans than peas does he grow? __60 − 40 = 20__
   He grows 20 more baskets of beans than peas.

4. What does Grampa Jim grow the most of? __tomatoes and carrots__

5. What does Grampa Jim grow the least of? __peas__

6. How many types of vegetables does Grampa Jim grow? __5__

7. How many baskets of vegetables does Grampa Jim grow all together? ____
   __90 + 60 + 90 + 40 + 70 = 350 baskets of vegetables all together__

47

Page 47

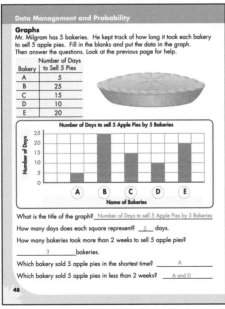

Data Management and Probability
Graphs
Mr. Milgram has 5 bakeries. He kept track of how long it took each bakery to sell 5 apple pies. Fill in the blanks and put the data in the graph. Then answer the questions. Look at the previous page for help.

Bakery	Number of Days to Sell 5 Pies
A	5
B	25
C	15
D	10
E	20

Number of Days to sell 5 Apple Pies by 5 Bakeries

What is the title of the graph? __Number of Days to sell 5 Apple Pies by 5 Bakeries__

How many days does each square represent? __5__ days.

How many bakeries took more than 2 weeks to sell 5 apple pies?
__3__ bakeries.

Which bakery sold 5 apple pies in the shortest time? __A__
Which bakery sold 5 apple pies in less than 2 weeks? __A and D__

48

Page 48

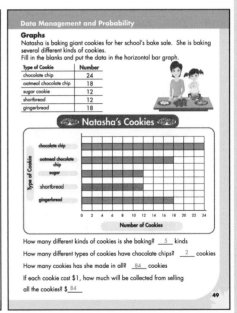

Data Management and Probability
Graphs
Natasha is baking giant cookies for her school's bake sale. She is baking several different kinds of cookies.
Fill in the blanks and put the data in the horizontal bar graph.

Type of Cookie	Number
chocolate chip	24
oatmeal chocolate chip	18
sugar cookie	12
shortbread	12
gingerbread	18

Natasha's Cookies

How many different kinds of cookies is she baking? __5__ kinds

How many different types of cookies have chocolate chips? __2__ cookies

How many cookies has she made in all? __84__ cookies

If each cookie cost $1, how much will be collected from selling all the cookies? $ __84__

49

Page 49

Solutions

Page 50

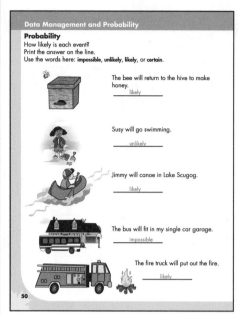

Data Management and Probability

Probability
How likely is each event?
Print the answer on the line.
Use the words here: **impossible, unlikely, likely,** or **certain.**

The bee will return to the hive to make honey.
_____likely_____

Susy will go swimming.
_____unlikely_____

Jimmy will canoe in Lake Scugog.
_____likely_____

The bus will fit in my single car garage.
_____impossible_____

The fire truck will put out the fire.
_____likely_____

50

Page 51

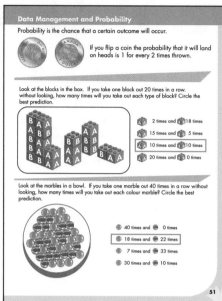

Data Management and Probability

Probability is the chance that a certain outcome will occur.

If you flip a coin the probability that it will land on heads is 1 for every 2 times thrown.

Look at the blocks in the box. If you take one block out 20 times in a row, without looking, how many times will you take out each type of block? Circle the best prediction.

🅰 2 times and 🅱 18 times
🅰 15 times and 🅱 5 times
🅰 10 times and 🅱 10 times
🅰 20 times and 🅱 0 times

Look at the marbles in a bowl. If you take one marble out 40 times in a row without looking, how many times will you take out each colour marble? Circle the best prediction.

🔵 40 times and ⚫ 0 times
🔵 18 times and ⚫ 22 times
🔵 7 times and ⚫ 33 times
🔵 30 times and ⚫ 10 times

51

Page 52

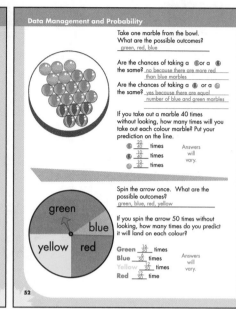

Data Management and Probability

Take one marble from the bowl.
What are the possible outcomes?
_____green, red, blue_____

Are the chances of taking a 🔴 or a 🔵 the same? _no because there are more red_
_____than blue marbles_____

Are the chances of taking a 🔵 or a 🟢 the same? _yes because there are equal_
_____number of blue and green marbles_____

If you take out a marble 40 times without looking, how many times will you take out each colour marble? Put your prediction on the line.

🔴 $\frac{20}{40}$ times   Answers
🔵 $\frac{10}{40}$ times   will
🟢 $\frac{10}{40}$ times   vary.

Spin the arrow once. What are the possible outcomes?
_____green, blue, red, yellow_____

If you spin the arrow 50 times without looking, how many times do you predict it will land on each colour?

Green $\frac{16}{51}$ times   Answers
Blue $\frac{8}{51}$ times   will
Yellow $\frac{12}{51}$ times   vary.
Red $\frac{12}{51}$ time

52

Page 53

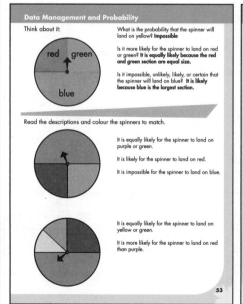

Data Management and Probability

Think about it:

What is the probability that the spinner will land on yellow? **Impossible**

Is it more likely for the spinner to land on red or green? **It is equally likely because the red and green section are equal size.**

Is it impossible, unlikely, likely, or certain that the spinner will land on blue? **It is likely because blue is the largest section.**

Read the descriptions and colour the spinners to match.

It is equally likely for the spinner to land on purple or green.
It is likely for the spinner to land on red.
It is impossible for the spinner to land on blue.

It is equally likely for the spinner to land on yellow or green.
It is more likely for the spinner to land on red than purple.

53

Page 54

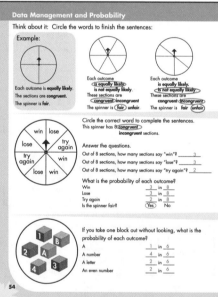

Data Management and Probability

Think about it: Circle the words to finish the sentences:

Example:

Each outcome is **equally likely.**
The sections are **congruent.**
The spinner is **fair.**

Each outcome
(is equally likely.)
is not equally likely.
These sections are
(congruent) incongruent
The spinner is **(fair)** unfair.

Each outcome
is equally likely.
(is not equally likely.)
These sections are
congruent **(incongruent)**
The spinner is fair **(unfair)**

Circle the correct word to complete the sentences. This spinner has 8 **(congruent)** incongruent sections.

Answer the questions.
Out of 8 sections, how many sections say "win"? _____3_____
Out of 8 sections, how many sections say "lose"? _____3_____
Out of 8 sections, how many sections say "try again"? _____2_____

What is the probability of each outcome?
Win $\frac{3}{8}$ in 8
Lose $\frac{3}{8}$ in 8
Try again $\frac{2}{8}$ in 8
Is the spinner fair?   **(Yes)**   No

If you take one block out without looking, what is the probability of each outcome?
A   _1_ in _6_
A number   _4_ in _6_
A letter   _2_ in _6_
An even number _2_ in _6_

54

Page 55

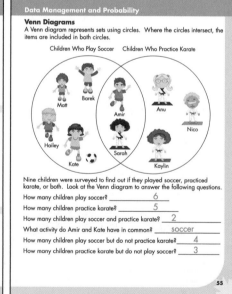

Data Management and Probability

Venn Diagrams
A Venn diagram represents sets using circles. Where the circles intersect, the items are included in both circles.

Children Who Play Soccer   Children Who Practice Karate

Matt   Barek   Amir   Anu   Nico
Hailey   Sarah   Kaylin
Kate

Nine children were surveyed to find out if they played soccer, practiced karate, or both. Look at the Venn diagram to answer the following questions.

How many children play soccer? _____6_____
How many children practice karate? _____5_____
How many children play soccer and practice karate? _____2_____
What activity do Amir and Kate have in common? _____soccer_____
How many children play soccer but do not practice karate? _____4_____
How many children practice karate but do not play soccer? _____3_____

55

Written by teachers working in the Canadian classroom

Reading

Grade **3**

Canadian Curriculum Press
Forward Learning

Friends in the Forest

- Reading comprehension
- Fact vs. opinion, fiction vs. non-fiction
- Reading resources and research skills
- Reading for pleasure and information
- And much more!

Elaine J. Kenny, B.Ed.

Grade 3 Reading

Contents

Syllables

To help you read a word you don't know, you can divide it into sections called **syllables**. Every **syllable** has a vowel. **Vowels** are **a e i o u**.

⇨ Example: pump · kin
Pumpkin has two **vowels** and two **syllables**.
Sound out **pump** and **kin** to make pumpkin.

Read the list of words and write each syllable you hear on the lines provided. The first one has been done for you.

	1st syllable	2nd syllable	3rd syllable	# of syllables
recess	re	cess	_____	2
example	_____	_____	_____	
because	_____	_____	_____	
anything	_____	_____	_____	
today	_____	_____	_____	
summer	_____	_____	_____	
excited	_____	_____	_____	
together	_____	_____	_____	
apple	_____	_____	_____	
better	_____	_____	_____	
another	_____	_____	_____	
pioneers	_____	_____	_____	

Compound Words

Sometimes two or more words are put together to make a new word called a **compound word**. To help read the new word, break it down into two smaller words and then read them together.

➪ Example: sand + box = sandbox
Sandbox is a **compound word**.

Read the list of words below. Draw a line between the words that make up the compound word. The first one is done for you.

sand | box   doghouse   breakfast

summertime   airplane   broomstick

dinnertime   timeline   campfire

nickname   pigpen   fingerprint

More Compound Words

Read the compound words list.

sailboats	sunburn	birthday	paintbrush	outdoors
barnyard	beehive	driveway	cardboard	sidewalk

Read these sentences. Fill in the blanks with the compound word that fits best from the list. The first one has been done for you.

After being in the sun all day, I realized I had a __sunburn__.

I always have a chocolate cake when it's my _____.

It's fun playing _____ in the summertime.

My dad parks his car in the _____.

Always clean your _____ with soap and water after you use it.

There are lots of _____ on the lake.

We get honey from a _____.

Remember to shovel the _____ in front of your house after it snows.

You can find cows and pigs in a _____.

Recycling _____ is a way to help our environment.

Following Directions

Following directions is a very important skill. You use it to find a new place, follow a recipe, or complete a task.

Read the directions on how to make a super sundae. Read the ingredient choices listed. Draw and label your sundae on the following page based on the directions.

1. Choose two types of ice cream and put two scoops of each in the sundae dish.
2. Next, choose your favourite sauce to pour on top.
3. Choose two toppings to sprinkle over the sauce.
4. Add as much fruit as you like.
5. Finally, add one cherry on top.

Ice Cream Flavours
vanilla
chocolate
butterscotch
strawberry

Sauces
chocolate
caramel
strawberry
hot fudge

Toppings
nuts
marshmallows
sprinkles
chocolate chips

Fruit
pineapple chunks
sliced strawberries
sliced banana
blueberries
cherries

Your Super Sundae!

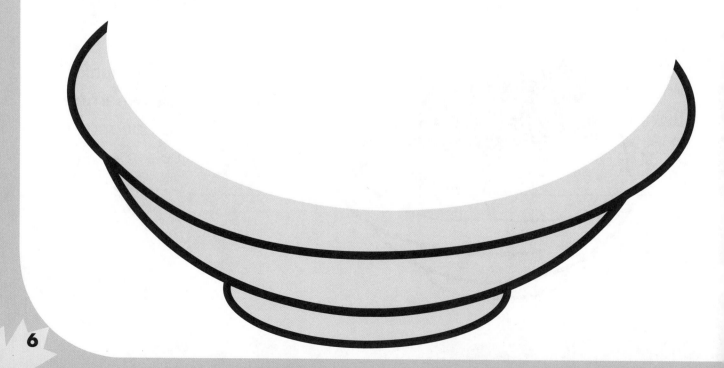

Reading a Recipe

You must carefully follow directions when completing a recipe in order for it to turn out. Read the recipe for Simple Chocolate Brownies. Answer the questions on the following page.

Simple Chocolate Brownies
Makes 12-24 Brownies

Ingredients

1/2 cup (125 ml) butter
2 squares unsweetened chocolate
1 cup (250 ml) sugar
2 eggs, well beaten
1/2 teaspoon (2 ml) vanilla
3/4 cup (175 ml) flour
1/4 teaspoon (1 ml) salt
1/2 cup (125 ml) chopped walnuts (optional)

Preparation

1. Preheat oven to 350° F
2. Melt butter and chocolate together over low heat. Remove from heat as soon as melted.
3. Slowly add beaten eggs stirring constantly.
4. Add remaining ingredients and stir.
5. Pour into a greased 8-inch (20 cm) square pan.
6. Bake for 25 to 30 minutes until a toothpick comes out clean.
7. Cool and cut into squares.

Reading a Recipe

Answer these questions about the Simple Chocolate Brownies recipe on previous page. Write your answer in complete sentences.

How many squares of chocolate does the recipe need?

_____

_____

What needs to be well beaten before mixing with something else?

_____

_____

At what temperature is the oven set?

_____

_____

How long do the brownies take to bake?

_____

_____

What do you do last? (check one)

_____ Preheat the oven to 350° F.

_____ Cut the cooled brownies into squares.

_____ Pour into a greased 8-inch (20 cm) square pan.

What two ingredients do you measure in teaspoons?

_____

_____

How many brownies does the recipe make?

_____

Sequencing

Sequencing means putting things in correct order. It is the order in which the events take place.

⇨ Example: I woke up, got out of bed, and went to the bathroom. After brushing my teeth, I got dressed, ate breakfast, and left for school.

Read the sentences below about brushing your teeth. Number them in the correct order from 1 through 7 in the boxes.

Spit out the toothpaste. ☐

Put toothbrush and toothpaste away. ☐

Move brush around in your mouth. ☐

Wet the toothbrush and toothpaste with water. ☐

Get out your toothbrush and the toothpaste. ☐

Rinse off toothbrush. ☐

Squeeze toothpaste onto your toothbrush. ☐

Sequencing

To understand the order in which things happen in a story, look for time order words like **first**, **next**, and **finally**.

Read the story. Answer the questions.

The Campfire

Samantha helped her father start a campfire. First, she cleared the fire pit. Next, she set up lots of kindling that would burn quickly and then added two big logs that would burn more slowly. After striking the match and lighting the fire, she waited a few minutes to see if the wood had caught fire. Finally, Samantha put a hot dog on a long stick and held it just above the fire until it was cooked.

Answer the questions in complete sentences.

What did Samantha do first?

_____

_____

What did Samantha do last?

_____

_____

What was one other thing Samantha did to start the campfire?

_____

_____

More Sequencing

Read the following sentences. Write them in the correct order on the lines provided.

Carving a Pumpkin

Carve a face into the pumpkin.
Bring the pumpkin home.
Put a candle in the pumpkin.
Get out a sharp knife.
Cut off the top and scoop out the seeds.
Pick a pumpkin from the patch.
Light the candle and set outside when dark.

1. _____

2. _____

3. _____

4. _____

5. _____

6. _____

7. _____

Compare and Contrast

If you **contrast** two things, you show how they are different. If you **compare** and **contrast** two things, you show how they are alike and how they are different.

Fill in the chart below to compare and contrast what it is like to live in Canada during the winter and during the summer.

Canadian Winter and Summer

	Alike	Different
Weather		
Activities		
Food		
Holidays		
Clothing		

Finding Hidden Meaning

At times, you may read something that has a phrase you need to interpret in order to understand the meaning.

⇨ Example: **She is as sweet as candy.**
This sentence means she's a very nice girl.

Read the sentences. Circle a, b, or c for the sentence that best explains what the first sentence means.

⇨ Example: One bad apple spoils the whole bushel.
a. The apples are in a bunch.
b. One bad person can have a bad affect on everyone around him or her.
c. Apples spoil.

Kill two birds with one stone.
a. You kill birds with stones.
b. Complete two tasks with one action.
c. Birds are dying.

Don't judge a book by its cover!
a. Don't read books with covers you don't like.
b. You must look inside the book to judge it.
c. You shouldn't judge a person by his or her looks alone.

Everyone is in the same boat.
a. Everyone is sailing together.
b. Everyone is facing the same problem.
c. The boat is big enough to carry many people.

Main Idea

The **main idea** is the most important meaning of something you read. It does not include less important details.

Read these passages. Answer the questions.

Ken is very active. He gets up early every morning and goes for a jog before school. Ken rides his bike to school instead of taking the bus.

What is the main idea?
   a. Ken likes school.
   b. Ken is fit.
   c. Ken likes to ride his bike.

Lisa developed a business plan. She decided to walk dogs for people in the neighbourhood. Lisa created posters and went door to door looking for customers. Lisa got so many customers that she had to hire her friend Elaine to help.

What is the main idea?
   a. Lisa is friendly.
   b. Lisa likes dogs.
   c. Lisa worked hard to make her plan work.

Main Idea

Remember that the **main idea** is the basic meaning of the reading material. It is the most important message in the writing.

Read the paragraph. Answer the questions.

Almost everyone likes to eat pizza. In fact, pizza is eaten all over the world. Many different toppings can be put on pizza. The most popular one in Canada is pepperoni. Pizza has ingredients from all four food groups. The crust is a grain product, the cheese is a milk product, the tomato sauce is a vegetable, and the pepperoni is meat. It can be a very healthy dinner if you add a salad on the side and a cold glass of milk.

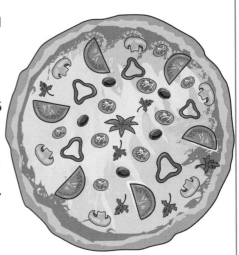

What is the main idea of the paragraph? Answer in a complete sentence.

_____

_____

_____

_____

Which of the following statements is **not true**? Circle a, b, c, or d.
   a. Pizza is a healthy dinner.
   b. Pizza is only sold in Canada.
   c. Pizza has ingredients from all four food groups.
   d. There are many different toppings that can be put on pizza.

Making Predictions

A good reader uses information in a text and what he or she already knows to think about what might happen next.

Read each sentence beginning. Circle the best sentence ending.
The first one has been done for you.

If you eat too much candy before going to bed, your stomach is likely to feel

    a. great
    (b. sick)
    c. empty

If you put water on a slice of bread, it is likely to get

    a. soggy
    b. bigger
    c. hard

If a dog bites you, you are likely to feel

    a. happy
    b. angry
    c. curious

If you leave a popsicle on the counter on a summer day, it is likely to

    a. stay the same
    b. harden
    c. melt

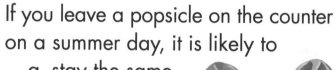

If you put your hand on a burning log, it is likely to

    a. hurt
    b. tickle
    c. feel great

If you work hard on an assignment, you are likely to

    a. fail
    b. get a good mark
    c. not learn anything

Making Predictions

Read each passage. Circle a, b, or c for the sentence that best answers each question.

Big Brother

Damian walks his little brother to school every day. Damian holds his hand and helps him safely cross the street. One day, Damian forgot his backpack at home. He had a math assignment in it that he needed for class. Damian always does his best at school.

Which sentence tells what will most likely happen next?

a. Damian will leave his brother alone and go home to get his backpack.

b. Damian will walk back home taking his little brother safely with him.

c. Damian will continue walking to school and not hand in his assignment.

The Zoo

Mazari went to the zoo with her father. It was a great day! She loved seeing all the animals and spending time outdoors with her dad. When Mazari got home, she told her mom about all the things she had seen at the zoo.

Which sentence tells what will likely happen next?

a. Mazari will forget all about her day.

b. Mazari will read all about different zoos.

c. Mazari's father will forbid her from going to the zoo again.

Making Predictions

Read the passage. Answer the question.

Basketball

Roshawn has never made a school team before. He used to be one of the shortest boys in his class, but this year he has grown so much that now he is the tallest. Every Saturday morning, Roshawn plays basketball at the community centre. He has learned how to dribble and shoot very well.

What do you think will happen when Roshawn tries out for the basketball team? Make a prediction.

_____

_____

Study the pictures. Answer the questions.

What do you think is going to happen to the flower? Make a prediction.

_____

_____

_____

_____

Why do you think so? _____

Facts and Opinions

A **fact** is something that is real and true. An **opinion** is a statement reflecting the writer's beliefs.

⇨ Examples: **Facts**

There are 7 days in a week.

The Canadian flag is red and white.

Opinions

Pizza is better than broccoli.

The Canadian flag is the most beautiful flag in the world.

Read each sentence. Put an **F** in the box if the sentence is a **fact**. Put an **O** in the box if the sentence is an **opinion**. The first one is done for you.

Boys are always taller than girls. **O**

July comes after June in the calendar year. ☐

Ottawa is in Canada. ☐

Dogs are smarter than cats. ☐

July 1st is Canada Day. ☐

Summer is everyone's favourite time of year. ☐

Eating an apple a day will keep the doctor away. ☐

If you find a penny and pick it up you will have good luck. ☐

Smoking is bad for your health. ☐

There is a maple leaf on Canada's flag. ☐

Maple syrup comes from maple trees. ☐

Drinking milk can make your bones stronger. ☐

Sorting Facts and Opinions

Good readers sort out information as they read. They decide if the information is a fact or an opinion.

Fact

When you don't know if something is a fact, you can look for proof that it is true. For example, if someone says it is two o'clock, you can check a clock to be sure. Sometimes, you need to look up a fact. Some of the sources you might use include Wikipedia, almanacs, textbooks, biographies, and encyclopedias. Facts answer the questions who, what, when, where, why, and how.

Opinion

An opinion is what the writer thinks or believes. It is the author's judgment on a certain topic. Opinions are found in many kinds of writing. They sometimes can be mistaken for facts. The editorial page of a newspaper is set aside for opinions. People can have different opinions based on the same set of facts.

Look at the pictures. Read each sentence. Write an **F** if the sentence is a **fact**. Write an **O** if the sentence is an **opinion**.

Canada

Japan

There are five flags. _____
The Canadian flag is the most beautiful. _____
The Irish flag is orange, green, and white. _____
The Japanese flag is easy to identify. _____
The United States of America's flag is red, white, and blue. _____
The Canadian flag is the most unique. _____
The flag of Sudan has the most colours. _____

Ireland

USA

Write another fact about the pictures.

Sudan

_____

Write another opinion about the pictures.

_____

Sorting Facts and Opinions

A piece of writing often includes both facts and opinions.
Read the paragraph. Answer the questions.

Lacrosse is Canada's national summer sport. First Nations people, who were the first people to live in what is now Canada, invented lacrosse many years ago as part of a ceremony. Later, other people who came to settle in Canada started to play the game too. Lacrosse can be played inside an arena or outside on a field. You will like to play lacrosse if you like to play hockey. You use a lacrosse stick and a hard rubber ball. Lacrosse is the best game ever!

Write "fact" or "opinion" next to each sentence.

Lacrosse is Canada's national summer sport. _____

Lacrosse is the best game ever! _____

First Nations people invented lacrosse many years ago. _____

You will like lacrosse if you like hockey. _____

Write another fact from the paragraph.

_____

_____

_____

_____

_____

Context Clues

Context clues are words in a sentence or surrounding sentences that help you understand a word you don't know.

⇨ Example: The dinosaur bones in the museum are **enormous**. They take up almost all the space in the room.

If you don't know what **enormous** means, you can figure it out from the next sentence: take up all the space in the room.

Underline the words that help you figure out the meaning of the green word or phrase. Answer the questions.

⇨ Example: The drive-in movie began after **dusk**, just after the sunset. What is the meaning of dusk?

   Dusk is when it is starting to get dark.

Paul is a **meteorologist**, a person who studies weather patterns. What is a meteorologist?

_____

After adding **fertilizer**, the plants in my garden grew quickly. They produced large, beautiful flowers. What is fertilizer?

_____

She said she could run a marathon without getting thirsty, but I felt **dubious** about it. What does dubious mean?

_____

After school, I'm always **ravenous**. I can't seem to get enough to eat to fill me up! What does ravenous mean?

_____

The twins show signs of **telepathy**. They can communicate with each other without speaking a word. What does telepathy mean?

_____

Fiction and Non-Fiction

Non-fiction books contain facts. They might tell about a real person like Terry Fox, or about real animals, places, or events.

Fiction books contain made up stories that come from the writer's imagination. They could be about aliens or talking animals or anything the writer thinks of. Some books include a mixture of some real events or people from the past and some make-believe events and characters. This is called historical fiction.

Look at the list of book titles below. Put them in either the fiction column or the non-fiction column.

Cinderella
Building the Canadian National Railway
Father Bear Bakes a Cake
How to Build a Birdhouse
The City Mouse and the Country Mouse
The Life of Alexander Graham Bell
Tom and Jerry Adventures
Canada's Lakes and Rivers

Fiction	Non-fiction
_____	_____
_____	_____
_____	_____
_____	_____

A Non-Fiction Story

Read the story. Answer the questions on the next page.

The School Trip

Poplar Road's Grade 3 class was going on a trip to the sugar bush to learn all about maple syrup. They had been studying early pioneers. They knew that pioneers had learned how to make maple syrup and use it as a sweetener from the First Nations people. The class had worked hard and their teacher, Mrs. Misner, had arranged the trip as a reward for all their hard work.

The bus pulled in front of the school and the students all boarded. They were off! After about 30 minutes, the bus pulled into a Conservation Area. It was beautiful! A guide named Susan met them as the students all filed out of the bus. She led the students along a path towards the sugar shack, pointing out the sap buckets along the way. Soon the group arrived at an area that had a beautiful fire going and a large black pot hanging over it. Susan explained to the students that the sap they had seen being collected along the way was boiling in the pot over the fire. She explained the steps needed to turn the sap into syrup.

Susan told the students to take a seat on the logs around the fire. Next, she went into the sugar shack and came out with plates piled high with pancakes for each student. Mrs. Misner was given a jug of maple syrup to pour over the pancakes. The students loved the treat and all agreed that Canadian maple syrup was one of the best things that the early pioneers learned to make from the First Nations people. It was a great day!

A Non-Fiction Story

After reading the non-fiction story, "The School Trip," answer these questions.
Write the main events in the order they happened in the story.

1._____

_____

2._____

_____

3._____

_____

4._____

_____

5._____

_____

Draw each event in the order that they happened in the story.

A Fictional Story

Read the story. Answer the questions on the next page.

Summer Camp

Jeffrey was nervous. In less than one week he was leaving to go to camp for the first time. Jeffrey had read about camp and his older brother Sam had gone for the last two summers, but he still couldn't help being scared. Jeffrey was always scared when he tried new things.

On Saturday morning, his mom and dad woke him at 8 o'clock so he could have a good breakfast before leaving for camp. Jeffrey's stomach flipped as he saw his bags beside the front door. He calmed himself down during breakfast by pretending he wasn't leaving, but that didn't last long. Before he knew it the car was packed and the family was on their way.

As they drove, Jeffrey's family told him funny stories about when they had been at camp. Sam talked about a time when he fell out of a canoe and got soaked. Jeffrey's mom talked about meeting lots of friends and the funny pranks they played on each other.

When they arrived at camp, Jeffrey met his counsellor and the rest of the boys in his cabin. He said a tearful goodbye to his family and then set up his sleeping bag and gear. That night Jeffrey found it really hard to get to sleep. All he could think about was his family.

The next morning finally came. After breakfast it was time for a canoe lesson. Jeff found out he liked something called "gunwale bobbing" and that the other boys in his cabin were really nice. Before he knew it, the day was over and it was time to go to sleep. The rest of the week flew by. Jeffrey tried many new things. He went canoeing and kayaking. He went hiking in the woods with a map and compass. Jeffrey even slept outdoors on the last night!

Jeffrey was sad when he woke up on the last morning. He couldn't believe how much fun camp had been. When his mom and dad arrived, Jeffrey gave them both a big hug and said he was counting down the days until next summer when he would be going to camp again!

A Fictional Story

Answer these questions about the fictional story, "Summer Camp". Write your answers in complete sentences.

Why was Jeffrey so nervous?

_____

_____

_____

What were some of the things his family did to help Jeffrey feel better?

_____

_____

_____

Was there a time when you were nervous about something?

_____

_____

_____

What did Jeffrey learn about himself while he was at camp?

_____

_____

_____

Setting

The **setting** of a story is when and where it takes place. It describes the time and different places in a story.

Read each description and circle the correct time and place.

Description	Time	Place
As I opened my eyes, I saw the bright sunlight shining on my bed. I quickly jumped up and scurried around to get dressed as fast as I could.	evening afternoon morning	school home hockey arena
Even though it was dark, I knew where we were. My mom was carrying the popcorn and I was carrying the drinks. We sat down and anxiously waited for it to start.	morning afternoon evening	gym movie theatre dentist
The mid-day sun shone into my eyes as I tried to catch my friends. I climbed up the slide, hoping to tag someone at the top.	morning afternoon evening	garage playground store

Reading Comprehension

Description	Time	Place
"Please, can't I stay up and watch the hockey game," I begged. "Sorry," said Mom. "Tomorrow you have a really early game yourself so you need your sleep."	morning afternoon evening	store school home
"Your assignment is due tomorrow, first thing in the morning. Please put up your chairs as you leave. See you tomorrow," said my teacher.	morning afternoon evening	playground school home
The stars were out as I ran up the driveway. I wanted to get to the T.V. before my brother so I could pick the show we were going to watch.	morning afternoon evening	museum school home

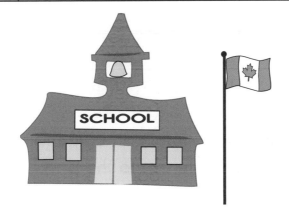

Reading Comprehension

Fiction

Read the story. Answer the questions on the next page.

A Trip to the Park
by Ahsan Rahim-Zada

Daniel and I stood with my dad at the entrance to the park. "Race you to the swings!" yelled Daniel. I ran so hard I felt my legs were going to fall off.

"Hey Dad, can you come and push us, pretty please?" My dad came over and pushed both of us at once! I went so high I felt like I could reach up and grab a piece of the clouds and bring it down. When we jumped off, I felt a little dizzy. "Let's go down the slide now," I said to Daniel.

"Mr. Morra, could you please push us down the slide?" asked Daniel. Then we went down zippy fast to the bottom. "Let's go on the monkey bars now," Daniel said.

Uh, oh, I thought. You see, the thing is Daniel is in Grade 4 and I am in Grade 3 and the monkey bars wobble. My dad says they are at least five feet high so you have to jump to get on them.

"Hurry up, Matthew!" yelled Daniel. So I walked slowly over, thinking, I can do this! Daniel had already done it so he was waiting on the other side. I jumped up and, yes, I grabbed the first bar! Only 9 more.

"Just think one hand, two hand," said Daniel.

"Okay, so one and two, one and two, one and two, one and two, one and two, one and two, one and two, one and two, one and two!"

"Matthew, you did it!" yelled Daniel.

"Way to go, Sport!" said my dad.

"Wow, I did it."

"Okay, guys, time to go," my dad said.

"Hey, Dad? Can we come back tomorrow?"

"Sure thing Matthew, and Daniel can come too."

So that was my most favourite trip to the park.

Fiction

After reading "A Trip to the Park," answer these questions.
Write your answers in complete sentences.

Why was Matthew so nervous?

_____

_____

_____

Why did Matthew start counting to himself?

_____

_____

_____

Have you ever felt this way before trying something new? What did you do?

_____

_____

_____

Do you think that having Daniel there helped Matthew complete the monkey bars? Why or why not?

_____

_____

_____

Setting

Draw the setting for "A Trip to the Park".

Non-Fiction Article

Read the article. Answer the questions about the article on the next page.

Canadian Pioneer Life

Canada was settled in the late 1700's and early 1800's by people from many parts of the world. These settlers were called pioneers.

Pioneers came to Canada for different reasons. Some came to start a new life in a country where there were many opportunities to better themselves. Others came to own land of their own. Many of the countries they had come from were crowded and had little food. Canada offered a new home with lots of space and food for everyone.

The pioneers came from many different countries. Pioneers travelled by boat from England, Scotland, Ireland, Italy, Germany, and France. Other pioneers lived in what is now the United States of America. These pioneers travelled north by land to Canada.

When the pioneers arrived in Canada they faced many hardships. Most of them had no experience with Canada's long and cold winters so their first winter here was really tough.

The First Nations people in the area were very helpful and taught the pioneers many survival skills to help them through the winter. In Canada, the pioneers were given free land, an axe, and some seed to plant crops. They had to clear the land and build their own homes with the logs they had cut. All their tools and utensils were made from the resources on their land. They either grew their own food, or found it in the forest. Life was hard. However, for most pioneers it was much better than the life they had left.

Non-Fiction Article

After reading the non-fiction article "Canadian Pioneer Life," answer these questions. Write your answers in complete sentences.

List three reasons why the early pioneers came to Canada.

1._____

_____

2._____

_____

3._____

List three places the early pioneers left to come to Canada.

1._____

2._____

3._____

Describe what the pioneers had to do when they came to Canada.

_____

_____

_____

_____

_____

Parts of a Book

A book is made up of different parts. Learning the parts of a book will help you become a better reader.

Book Cover

A book cover is the first thing you see when reading a book. Often the title will give you a hint about what the book is about. If there is a picture too, it helps you predict what the book might be about. The book cover includes the title of the book and the author's name.

⇨ Example:

Book Title
Picture helps predict what the book is about.

Author's Name

Prediction: This book is probably about a trip to a far away place that includes a plane ride.

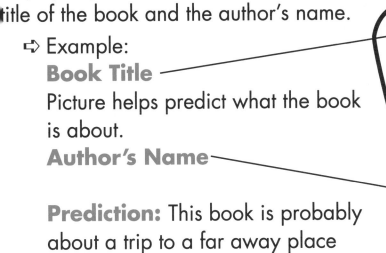

Read the book cover. Predict what the book is about.

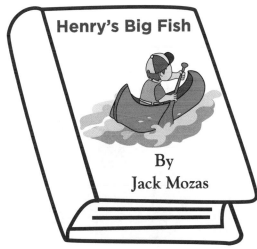

Title: _____

Author: _____

Prediction: _____

Book Cover

Read the book covers. Predict what the book is about.

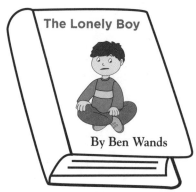

Title: _____

Author: _____

Prediction: _____

Title: _____

Author: _____

Prediction: _____

Title: _____

Author: _____

Prediction: _____

Book Cover

Design a book cover of your own!

What do you think a reader might predict about the book from your cover?

_____

_____

Book Cover

Draw a line to match each cover to its pages. Underline the books that could be non-fiction (true stories). Circle the books that could be fiction (make-believe stories).

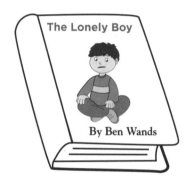

Table of Contents

The **table of contents** lists the titles of the chapters in the book and the page that each chapter starts on. In a non-fiction book, the chapter titles tell you what information you will find in each chapter.

Early Settlers
Table of Contents

Use the table of contents above to answer these questions.

What is the name of the chapter that begins on page 23?

_____

If you want to learn more about the First Nations, where would you look?

_____

Where would you look to find out why the settlers came to Canada?

_____

Where would you learn about what the early settlers ate?

_____

Glossary

A **glossary** is usually found at the back of a book. It lists specific words from the book and tells what those words mean. It is like a dictionary made just for that book. Read the glossary below. Answer the questions.

> conifers (con-i-fers) — trees or bushes that have waxy, needle-like or scaly leaves; most of these trees are evergreens.
>
> deciduous (de-cid-u-ous) — trees that shed their leaves in the fall
>
> legume (le-gume) — dry fruit with seeds attached to its inner wall; an example is a pea pod
>
> nectar (nec-tar) — a sweet, sticky substance produced by plants to attract insects

Answer these questions in complete sentences.

What type of tree loses its leaves in the fall?

_____

What is a legume?

_____

What are two types of trees?

_____

How many syllables in the word deciduous?

_____

What attracts insects?

_____

Index

An **index** is found at the back of a book. It lists the topics in the book and the pages where you will find information about those topics in the book. Indexes are found mostly in non-fiction books. The index is always in alphabetical order. Read the index below. Answer the questions.

Index

Arrows 5, 6, 7, 8
Bones 19, 20
Dwellings 39, 40, 54, 55, 56
Food 9, 10, 11, 12
Hunting Techniques . 26, 27, 28, 29, 30
Nomadic People. 41, 42, 43
Totem Poles 23, 24, 25
Wigwams 39

Answer these questions in complete sentences.

On what pages would you look to find out more about totem poles?

_____

What topic in the book starts on page 26?

_____

What do you learn about on page 9?

_____

What two things can you find on page 39?

_____

Where would you look to find out about hunting techniques?

_____

Review – Parts of the Book Match-Up

Draw a line from Column A to the correct definition in Column B.

Column A

glossary

book cover

table of contents

chapter heading

index

Column B

tells the title and author of the book

tells about what the chapter is all about

lists words used in the book and their meanings

shows where to look up information on a topic in the book

lists the chapters and the pages they start on

Dictionary, Encyclopedia, and Atlas

Resources

The material you read to help you learn about, research, and understand a topic are called reading resources. Dictionaries, encyclopedias, and atlases are examples of resources. These resources are available as books and on the internet.

Dictionary

A dictionary contains lots and lots of words. A dictionary is used to learn how to say words, spell words, and understand what words mean. The words in a dictionary are always in alphabetical order.

Encyclopedia

An encyclopedia has lots of information about many different topics in it. An encyclopedia is a good place to start when researching people, places, and things. It could be a book or an on-line resource such as Wikipedia.

Atlas

An atlas is packed with information about specific places like countries or cities and geographical features such as mountains, rivers, and oceans. An atlas contains lots of maps, charts, and graphs to help you. It is a good resource when you need to answer geography questions.

Research Skills

Read the following sentences. Write what resource you would use to answer the questions: dictionary, encyclopedia, or atlas?

➪ Example: Where is Ireland? _____**Atlas**_____

How do cars accelerate? _____

What does the word "knight" mean? _____

Where is the Atlantic Ocean? _____

Why do hummingbirds flap their wings so quickly? _____

How many syllables are in the word "geography"? _____

Who was Terry Fox and what did he do? _____

Which country is south of Canada? _____

Did Canada fight in Word War I? _____

What does the word "apothecary" mean? _____

Is "a-n-t" the correct way to spell the word that refers to a small insect?

_____

Where is Victoria? _____

Autobiographies

An **autobiography** is a book that tells the true story of a person's life. It is always written by the person who is the topic of the book. Answer the questions about yourself in complete sentences.

Where were you born?

_____

_____

Who are the members of your family?

_____

What activities do you like to do?

_____

What is your favourite subject in school? Why is it your favourite?

_____

What is your favourite television show? Why is it your favourite?

_____

How many pets have you had? What kind of pet would you like to have now?

_____

If you could do anything when you grow up, what would you like to do?

_____

Biographies

A **biography** is a book that tells the true story of a person's life. It is always written by a person who is not the topic of the book. It can be about someone who is alive now or someone who was alive a long time ago.

Examples of some biographies:

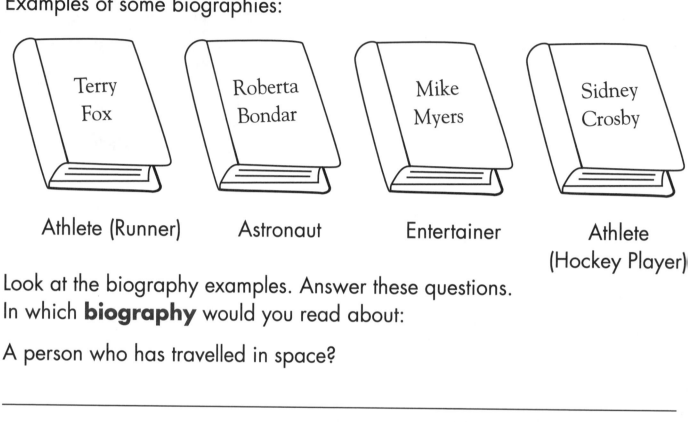

Terry Fox	Roberta Bondar	Mike Myers	Sidney Crosby
Athlete (Runner)	Astronaut	Entertainer	Athlete (Hockey Player)

Look at the biography examples. Answer these questions.
In which **biography** would you read about:

A person who has travelled in space?

_____

A person who has starred in movies?

_____

A person who spends lots of time on the ice?

_____

A person who likes to keep moving?

_____

Which biography would you like to read? Why?

_____

Reading a Letter

A **letter** is a form of communication between people.

> *August 29, 20XX*
>
> Dear Grandma,
> I'm writing to let you know how my summer has been. It has been so long since I've seen you and I really miss our talks.
>   In July, I spent two weeks at camp. I had a great time swimming and canoeing. I met lots of new friends. August was spent at the cottage where I learned to play chess. It is a great game! I love sleeping in and having lots of free time to do fun things.
>   School is nearly here. I'm not looking forward to getting up early every day or having homework to do at night. I hope to see you soon.
>
>   Lots of love,
>   Brad

Read the letter.
Answer each question with yes or no.

Did Brad like camp? _____

Is Brad looking forward to school? _____

Did Brad learn to play chess? _____

Could Brad sleep in at the cottage? _____

Does Brad like to go canoeing? _____

Has Brad seen his Grandma lately? _____

Write a Letter

Write your own letter to a friend describing your last special family day.

Posters

A **poster** is used to display information in words and pictures. It uses both words and pictures so the reader can understand the full meaning of the poster. Often important information is written in larger letters so that the reader can easily see it.

FOUND CAT
She was found at
11 Alberta Place on
Saturday, October 22

She has an orange coat with small
patches of white on her belly.
Her eyes are blue and her tail is bent.

She is really friendly.

If she is yours please call:
Elaine at 416-555-1234

Read the poster. Circle the correct answer or answer the questions in complete sentences.

The cat is   white   orange   grey

She has a bent   whisker   ear   tail

She was found on   October 22   January 9   September 16

How can you reach the person who made the poster?

_____

Is the cat friendly?

_____

Design a Poster

Design a poster about something you want to sell.

Remember to include both words and pictures.

Remember to include a way for the reader to reach you.

Advertisements and Flyers

An advertisement or flyer is used by stores to display the things they sell and the price. It is important to be able to read them in order to save money where possible.

CLAIRE'S CANDY STORE

Lollipops
Sale: 5 for $1.00
Regular: 50¢ each

Licorice
Sale: 99¢ for 250 g pack
Regular: $1.98 for 250 g pack

Chocolate Bars
Sale: 2 for $1.00
Regular: 89¢ each

Jawbreakers
Sale: 4 for $1.00
Regular: 50¢ each

Gummy Bears
Sale: $2.99 for 454 g pack
Regular: $3.99 for 454 g pack

Jube Jubes
Sale: $1.99 for 454 g pack
Regular: $3.49 for 454 g pack

Sale on until September 5, 20XX

Advertisements and Flyers

Read the advertisement/flyer on the previous page.
Circle **true** or **false** after each sentence.

The jube jubes cost $1.99.	true	false
The lollipops used to be 50¢ each.	true	false
The licorice is the least expensive candy.	true	false
Chocolate bars are 89¢ on sale.	true	false
Jawbreakers are 3 for a dollar.	true	false
Gummy bears are less expensive than jube jubes.	true	false

Answer these questions in complete sentences.

What is your favourite kind of candy? Why is it your favourite?

_____

_____

_____

Eating candy too much is not good for you. Why?

_____

_____

_____

Great Books for Kids

These are some books that are recommended by kids to read alone or with a grown-up. Ask a grown-up to go to the library with you, pick one out, and get reading! Tell a friend about the books you like!

Alligator Pie by Dennis Lee
Anne of Green Gables by Lucy Maud Montgomery
The Cremation of Sam McGee by Robert W. Service
Emma's Magic Winter by Jean Little
The Hockey Sweater by Roch Carrier
The Incredible Journey by Sheila Burnford
Owls in the Family by Farley Mowat
The Trumpet of the Swan by E.B. White
Burp! The Most Interesting Book You'll Ever Read About Eating
  by Diane Swanson
The Boxcar Children by Gertrude Chandler Warner
  (this one has over a hundred books in the series!)

Book Log

Keep track of the books you read and what you like.
Write the title and author on the line and then add your comments.

Title and Author:

_____

_____

Circle your thoughts: I loved it!   It was good   Just okay   Not for me

Title and Author:

_____

_____

Circle your thoughts: I loved it!   It was good   Just okay   Not for me

Title and Author:

_____

_____

Circle your thoughts: I loved it!   It was good   Just okay   Not for me

Title and Author:

_____

_____

Circle your thoughts: I loved it!   It was good   Just okay   Not for me

Title and Author:

_____

_____

Circle your thoughts: I loved it!   It was good   Just okay   Not for me

Title and Author:

_____

_____

Circle your thoughts: I loved it!   It was good   Just okay   Not for me

Title and Author:

_____

_____

Circle your thoughts: I loved it!   It was good   Just okay   Not for me

Title and Author:

_____

_____

Circle your thoughts: I loved it!   It was good   Just okay   Not for me

Title and Author:

_____

_____

Circle your thoughts: I loved it!   It was good   Just okay   Not for me

Solutions

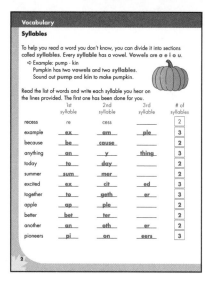

Page 2

Page 3

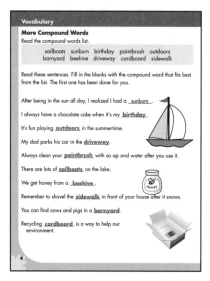

Page 4

Page 2 — Vocabulary: Syllables

To help you read a word you don't know, you can divide it into sections called **syllables**. Every syllable has a vowel. Vowels are a e i o u.

↪ Example: pump · kin
Pumpkin has two **vowels** and two **syllables**.
Sound out **pump** and **kin** to make pumpkin.

Read the list of words and write each syllable you hear on the lines provided. The first one has been done for you.

	1st syllable	2nd syllable	3rd syllable	# of syllables
recess	re	cess		2
example	ex	am	ple	3
because	be	cause		2
anything	an	y	thing	3
today	to	day		2
summer	sum	mer		2
excited	ex	cit	ed	3
together	to	geth	er	3
apple	ap	ple		2
better	bet	ter		2
another	an	oth	er	3
pioneers	pi	on	eers	3

Page 3 — Vocabulary: Compound Words

Sometimes two or more words are put together to make a new word called a **compound word**. To help read the new word, break it down into two smaller words and then read them together.

↪ Example: sand + box = sandbox
Sandbox is a **compound word**.

Read the list of words below. Draw a line between the words that make up the compound word. The first one is done for you.

sand | box   dog|house   break|fast
summer|time   air|plane   broom|stick
dinner|time   time|line   camp|fire
nick|name   pig|pen   finger|print

Page 4 — Vocabulary: More Compound Words

Read the compound words list.

sailboats sunburn birthday paintbrush outdoors
barnyard beehive driveway cardboard sidewalk

Read these sentences. Fill in the blanks with the compound word that fits best from the list. The first one has been done for you.

After being in the sun all day, I realized I had a _sunburn_.

I always have a chocolate cake when it's my _birthday_.

It's fun playing _outdoors_ in the summertime.

My dad parks his car in the _driveway_.

Always clean your _paintbrush_ with soap and water after you use it.

There are lots of _sailboats_ on the lake.

We get honey from a _beehive_.

Remember to shovel the _sidewalk_ in front of your house after it snows.

You can find cows and pigs in a _barnyard_.

Recycling _cardboard_ is a way to help our environment.

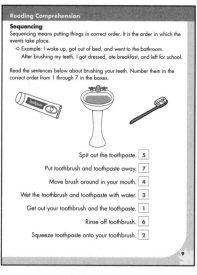

Page 7

Page 7 — Reading Comprehension: Reading a Recipe

You must carefully follow directions when completing a recipe in order for it to turn out. Read the recipe for Simple Chocolate Brownies. Answer the questions on the following page.

Simple Chocolate Brownies
Makes 12-24 Brownies

Ingredients
1/2 cup (125 ml) butter
2 squares unsweetened chocolate
1 cup (250 ml) sugar
2 eggs, well beaten
1/2 teaspoon (2 ml) vanilla
3/4 cup (175 ml) flour
1/4 teaspoon (1 ml) salt
1/2 cup (125 ml) chopped walnuts (optional)

Preparation
1. Preheat oven to 350° F
2. Melt butter and chocolate together over low heat. Remove from heat as soon as melted.
3. Slowly add beaten eggs stirring constantly.
4. Add remaining ingredients and stir.
5. Pour into a greased 8-inch (20 cm) square pan.
6. Bake for 25 to 30 minutes until a toothpick comes out clean.
7. Cool and cut into squares.

Page 8

Page 8 — Reading Comprehension: Reading a Recipe

Answer these questions about the Simple Chocolate Brownies recipe on previous page. Write your answer in complete sentences.

How many squares of chocolate does the recipe need?
The recipe needs two squares of chocolate.

What needs to be well beaten before mixing with something else?
The eggs need to be well beaten.

At what temperature is the oven set?
The oven is set at 350 degrees F.

How long do the brownies take to bake?
The brownies should bake for 25 to 30 minutes.

What do you do last? (check one)
____ Preheat the oven to 350° F.
_✓_ Cut the cooled brownies into squares.
____ Pour into a greased 8-inch (20 cm) square pan.

What two ingredients do you measure in teaspoons?
You measure vanilla and salt in teaspoons.

How many brownies does the recipe make?
The recipe makes 12 to 24 brownies.

Page 9

Page 9 — Reading Comprehension: Sequencing

Sequencing means putting things in correct order. It is the order in which the events take place.

↪ Example: I woke up, got out of bed, and went to the bathroom. After brushing my teeth, I got dressed, ate breakfast, and left for school.

Read the sentences below about brushing your teeth. Number them in the correct order from 1 through 7 in the boxes.

Spit out the toothpaste.	5
Put toothbrush and toothpaste away.	7
Move brush around in your mouth.	4
Wet the toothbrush and toothpaste with water.	3
Get out your toothbrush and the toothpaste.	1
Rinse off toothbrush.	6
Squeeze toothpaste onto your toothbrush.	2

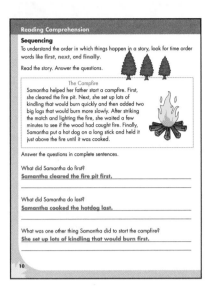

Reading Comprehension

Sequencing

To understand the order in which things happen in a story, look for time order words like **first, next,** and **finally.**

Read the story. Answer the questions.

The Campfire

Samantha helped her father start a campfire. First, she cleared the fire pit. Next, she set up lots of kindling that would burn quickly and then added two big logs that would burn more slowly. After striking the match and lighting the fire, she waited a few minutes to see if the wood had caught fire. Finally, Samantha put a hot dog on a long stick and held it just above the fire until it was cooked.

Answer the questions in complete sentences.

What did Samantha do first?
Samantha cleared the fire pit first.

What did Samantha do last?
Samantha cooked the hotdog last.

What was one other thing Samantha did to start the campfire?
She set up lots of kindling that would burn first.

10

Page 10

Reading Comprehension

More Sequencing

Read the following sentences. Write them in the correct order on the lines provided.

Carving a Pumpkin
Carve a face into the pumpkin.
Bring the pumpkin home.
Put a candle in the pumpkin.
Get out a sharp knife.
Cut off the top and scoop out the seeds.
Pick a pumpkin from the patch.
Light the candle and set outside when dark.

1. **Pick a pumpkin from the patch.**

2. **Bring the pumpkin home.**

3. **Get out a sharp knife.**

4. **Cut off the top and scoop out the seeds.**

5. **Carve a face into the pumpkin.**

6. **Put a candle in the pumpkin.**

7. **Light the candle and set outside when dark.**

11

Page 11

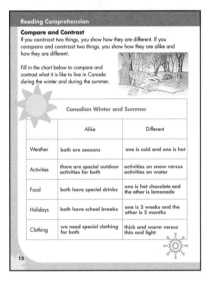

Reading Comprehension

Compare and Contrast

If you **contrast** two things, you show how they are different. If you **compare** two things, you show how they are alike and how they are different.

Fill in the chart below to compare and contrast what it is like to live in Canada during the winter and during the summer.

Canadian Winter and Summer

	Alike	Different
Weather	both are seasons	one is cold and one is hot
Activities	there are special outdoor activities for both	activities on snow versus activities on water
Food	both have special drinks	one is hot chocolate and the other is lemonade
Holidays	both have school breaks	one is 2 weeks and the other is 2 months
Clothing	we need special clothing for both	thick and warm versus thin and light

12

Page 12

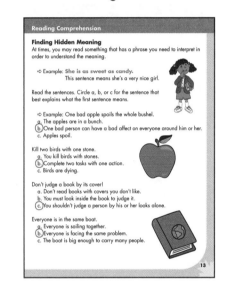

Reading Comprehension

Finding Hidden Meaning

At times, you may read something that has a phrase you need to interpret in order to understand the meaning.

↪ Example: **She is as sweet as candy.**
This sentence means she's a very nice girl.

Read the sentences. Circle a, b, or c for the sentence that best explains what the first sentence means.

↪ Example: One bad apple spoils the whole bushel.
a. The apples are in a bunch.
(b.) One bad person can have a bad affect on everyone around him or her.
c. Apples spoil.

Kill two birds with one stone.
a. You kill birds with stones.
(b.) Complete two tasks with one action.
c. Birds are dying.

Don't judge a book by its cover!
a. Don't read books with covers you don't like.
b. You must look inside the book to judge it.
(c.) You shouldn't judge a person by his or her looks alone.

Everyone is in the same boat.
a. Everyone is sailing together.
(b.) Everyone is facing the same problem.
c. The boat is big enough to carry many people.

13

Page 13

Reading Comprehension

Main Idea

The **main idea** is the most important meaning of something you read. It does not include less important details.

Read these passages. Answer the questions.

Ken is very active. He gets up early every morning and goes for a jog before school. Ken rides his bike to school instead of taking the bus.

What is the main idea?
a. Ken likes school.
(b.) Ken is fit.
c. Ken likes to ride his bike.

Lisa developed a business plan. She decided to walk dogs for people in the neighbourhood. Lisa created posters and went door to door looking for customers. Lisa got so many customers that she had to hire her friend Elaine to help.

What is the main idea?
a. Lisa is friendly.
b. Lisa likes dogs.
(c.) Lisa worked hard to make her plan work.

14

Page 14

Reading Comprehension

Main Idea

Remember that the **main idea** is the basic meaning of the reading material. It is the most important message in the writing.

Read the paragraph. Answer the questions.

Almost everyone likes to eat pizza. In fact, pizza is eaten all over the world. Many different toppings can be put on pizza. The most popular one in Canada is pepperoni. Pizza has ingredients from all four food groups. The crust is a grain product, the cheese is a milk product, the tomato sauce is a vegetable, and the pepperoni is meat. It can be a very healthy dinner if you add a salad on the side and a cold glass of milk.

What is the main idea of the paragraph? Answer in a complete sentence.

The main idea is that pizza is a popular and healthy food.

Which of the following statements is **not true**? Circle a, b, c, or d.
a. Pizza is a healthy dinner.
(b.) Pizza is only sold in Canada.
c. Pizza has ingredients from all four food groups.
d. There are many different toppings that can be put on pizza.

15

Page 15

Solutions

Page 16

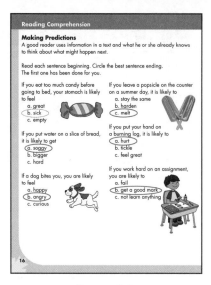

Reading Comprehension

Making Predictions
A good reader uses information in a text and what he or she already knows to think about what might happen next.

Read each sentence beginning. Circle the best sentence ending. The first one has been done for you.

If you eat too much candy before going to bed, your stomach is likely to feel
a. great
b. sick (circled)
c. empty

If you put water on a slice of bread, it is likely to get
a. soggy (circled)
b. bigger
c. hard

If a dog bites you, you are likely to feel
a. happy
b. angry (circled)
c. curious

If you leave a popsicle on the counter on a summer day, it is likely to
a. stay the same
b. harden
c. melt (circled)

If you put your hand on a burning log, it is likely to
a. hurt (circled)
b. tickle
c. feel great

If you work hard on an assignment, you are likely to
a. fail
b. get a good mark (circled)
c. not learn anything

Page 17

Reading Comprehension

Making Predictions
Read each passage. Circle a, b, or c for the sentence that best answers each question.

Big Brother
Damian walks his little brother to school every day. Damian holds his hand and helps him safely cross the street. One day, Damian forgot his backpack at home. He had a math assignment in it that he needed for class. Damian always does his best at school.

Which sentence tells what will most likely happen next?

a. Damian will leave his brother alone and go home to get his backpack.
b. Damian will walk back home taking his little brother safely with him. (circled)
c. Damian will continue walking to school and not hand in his assignment.

The Zoo
Mazari went to the zoo with her father. It was a great day! She loved seeing all the animals and spending time outdoors with her dad. When Mazari got home, she told her mom about all the things she had seen at the zoo.

Which sentence tells what will likely happen next?

a. Mazari will forget all about her day.
b. Mazari will read all about different zoos. (circled)
c. Mazari's father will forbid her from going to the zoo again.

Page 18

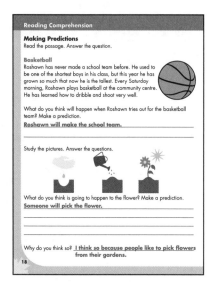

Reading Comprehension

Making Predictions
Read the passage. Answer the question.

Basketball
Roshawn has never made a school team before. He used to be one of the shortest boys in his class, but this year he has grown so much that now he is the tallest. Every Saturday morning, Roshawn plays basketball at the community centre. He has learned how to dribble and shoot very well.

What do you think will happen when Roshawn tries out for the basketball team? Make a prediction.
Roshawn will make the school team.

Study the pictures. Answer the questions.

What do you think is going to happen to the flower? Make a prediction.
Someone will pick the flower.

Why do you think so? **I think so because people like to pick flowers from their gardens.**

Page 19

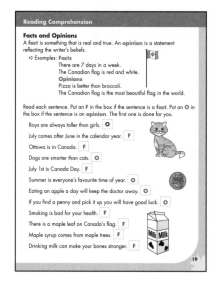

Reading Comprehension

Facts and Opinions
A fact is something that is real and true. An opinion is a statement reflecting the writer's beliefs.

⇨ Examples: **Facts**
There are 7 days in a week.
The Canadian flag is red and white.
Opinions
Pizza is better than broccoli.
The Canadian flag is the most beautiful flag in the world.

Read each sentence. Put an F in the box if the sentence is a fact. Put an O in the box if the sentence is an opinion. The first one is done for you.

Boys are always taller than girls. **O**
July comes after June in the calendar year. **F**
Ottawa is in Canada. **F**
Dogs are smarter than cats. **O**
July 1st is Canada Day. **F**
Summer is everyone's favourite time of year. **O**
Eating an apple a day will keep the doctor away. **O**
If you find a penny and pick it up you will have good luck. **O**
Smoking is bad for your health. **F**
There is a maple leaf on Canada's flag. **F**
Maple syrup comes from maple trees. **F**
Drinking milk can make your bones stronger. **F**

Page 20

Reading Comprehension

Sorting Facts and Opinions
Good readers sort out information as they read. They decide if the information is a fact or an opinion.

Fact
When you don't know if something is a fact, you can look for proof that it is true. For example, if someone says it is two o'clock, you can check a clock to be sure. Sometimes, you need to look up a fact. Some of the sources you might use include Wikipedia, almanacs, textbooks, biographies, and encyclopedias. Facts answer the questions who, what, when, where, why, and how.

Opinion
An opinion is what the writer thinks or believes. It is the author's judgment on a certain topic. Opinions are found in many kinds of writing. They sometimes can be mistaken for facts. The editorial page of a newspaper is set aside for opinions. People can have different opinions based on the same set of facts.

Look at the pictures. Read each sentence. Write an F if the sentence is a fact. Write an O if the sentence is an opinion.

There are five flags. **F**
The Canadian flag is the most beautiful. **O**
The Irish flag is orange, green, and white. **F**
The Japanese flag is easy to identify. **O**
The United States of America's flag is red, white, and blue. **F**
The Canadian flag is the most unique. **O**
The flag of Sudan has the most colours. **F**

Write another fact about the pictures.
Another fact is that the flags all have some white on them.

Write another opinion about the pictures.
Red is the best colour to have on a flag.

Page 21

Reading Comprehension

Sorting Facts and Opinions
A piece of writing often includes both facts and opinions. Read the paragraph. Answer the questions.

Lacrosse is Canada's national summer sport. First Nations people, who were the first people to live in what is now Canada, invented lacrosse many years ago as part of a ceremony. Later, other people who came to settle in Canada started to play the game too. Lacrosse can be played inside an arena or outside on a field. You will like to play lacrosse if you like to play hockey. You use a lacrosse stick and a hard rubber ball. Lacrosse is the best game ever!

Write "fact" or "opinion" next to each sentence.

Lacrosse is Canada's national summer sport. **Fact**
Lacrosse is the best game ever! **Opinion**
First Nations people invented lacrosse many years ago. **Fact**
You will like lacrosse if you like hockey. **Opinion**

Write another fact from the paragraph.
You play with a stick and hard rubber ball.

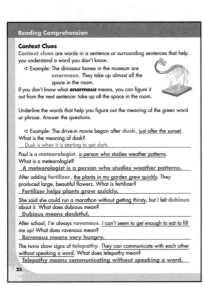

Page 22

Reading Comprehension

Context Clues

Context clues are words in a sentence or surrounding sentences that help you understand a word you don't know.

➪ Example: The dinosaur bones in the museum are **enormous**. They take up almost all the space in the room.

If you don't know what **enormous** means, you can figure it out from the next sentence: take up all the space in the room.

Underline the words that help you figure out the meaning of the green word or phrase. Answer the questions.

➪ Example: The drive-in movie began after **dusk**, just after the sunset.
What is the meaning of dusk?
Dusk is when it is starting to get dark.

Paul is a **meteorologist**, a person who studies weather patterns.
What is a meteorologist?
A meteorologist is a person who studies weather patterns.

After adding **fertilizer**, the plants in my garden grew quickly. They produced large, beautiful flowers. What is fertilizer?
Fertilizer helps plants grow quickly.

She said she could run a marathon without getting thirsty, but I felt **dubious** about it. What does dubious mean?
Dubious means doubtful.

After school, I'm always **ravenous**. I can't seem to get enough to eat to fill me up! What does ravenous mean?
Ravenous means very hungry.

The twins show signs of **telepathy**. They can communicate with each other without speaking a word. What does telepathy mean?
Telepathy means communicating without speaking a word.

22

Page 23

Reading Comprehension

Fiction and Non-Fiction

Non-fiction books contain facts. They might tell about a real person like Terry Fox, or about real animals, places, or events.

Fiction books contain made up stories that come from the writer's imagination. They could be about aliens or talking animals or anything the writer thinks of. Some books include a mixture of some real events or people from the past and some make-believe events and characters. This is called historical fiction.

Look at the list of book titles below. Put them in either the fiction column or the non-fiction column.

Cinderella
Building the Canadian National Railway
Father Bear Bakes a Cake
How to Build a Birdhouse
The City Mouse and the Country Mouse
The Life of Alexander Graham Bell
Tom and Jerry Adventures
Canada's Lakes and Rivers

Fiction	Non-fiction
Cinderella	Building the Canadian National Railway
Father Bear Bakes a Cake	
The City Mouse and the Country Mouse	How to Build a Birdhouse
	The Life of Alexander Graham Bell
Tom and Jerry Adventures	
	Canada's Lakes and Rivers

23

Page 24

Reading Comprehension

A Non-Fiction Story

Read the story. Answer the questions on the next page.

The School Trip

Poplar Road's Grade 3 class was going on a trip to the sugar bush to learn all about maple syrup. They had been studying early pioneers. They knew that pioneers had learned how to make maple syrup and use it as a sweetener from the First Nations people. The class had worked hard and their teacher, Mrs. Misner, had arranged the trip as a reward for all their hard work.

The bus pulled in front of the school and the students all boarded. They were off! After about 30 minutes, the bus pulled into a Conservation Area. It was beautiful! A guide named Susan met them as the students all filed out of the bus. She led the students along a path towards the sugar shack, pointing out the sap buckets along the way. Soon the group arrived at an area that had a beautiful fire going and a large black pot hanging over it. Susan explained to the students that the sap they had seen being collected along the way was boiling in the pot over the fire. She explained the steps needed to turn the sap into syrup.

Susan told the students to take a seat on the logs around the fire. Next, she went into the sugar shack and came out with plates piled high with pancakes for each student. Mrs. Misner was given a jug of maple syrup to pour over the pancakes. The students loved the treat and all agreed that Canadian maple syrup was one of the best things that the early pioneers learned to make from the First Nations people. It was a great day!

24

Page 25

Reading Comprehension

A Non-Fiction Story

After reading the non-fiction story, "The School Trip," answer these questions. Write the main events in the order they happened in the story.

1. The class was going on a trip as a reward for hard work.

2. A guide named Susan met them when they arrived at the Conservation Area.

3. Susan showed them how maple syrup was made by pioneers.

4. Susan gave each student pancakes.

5. Mrs. Misner gave everyone syrup to put on their pancakes.

Draw each event in the order that they happened in the story.

25

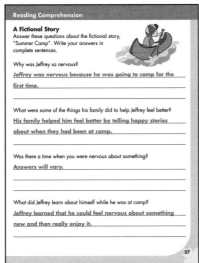

Page 27

Reading Comprehension

A Fictional Story

Answer these questions about the fictional story, "Summer Camp". Write your answers in complete sentences.

Why was Jeffrey so nervous?
Jeffrey was nervous because he was going to camp for the first time.

What were some of the things his family did to help Jeffrey feel better?
His family helped him feel better by telling happy stories about when they had been at camp.

Was there a time when you were nervous about something?
Answers will vary.

What did Jeffrey learn about himself while he was at camp?
Jeffrey learned that he could feel nervous about something new and then really enjoy it.

27

Page 28

Reading Comprehension

Setting

The setting of a story is when and where it takes place. It describes the time and different places in a story.

Read each description and circle the correct time and place.

Description	Time	Place
As I opened my eyes, I saw the bright sunlight shining on my bed. I quickly jumped up and scurried around to get dressed as fast as I could.	evening / afternoon / (morning)	school / (home) / hockey arena
Even though it was dark, I knew where we were. My mom was carrying the popcorn and I was carrying the drinks. We sat down and anxiously waited for it to start.	morning / afternoon / (evening)	gym / (movie theatre) / dentist
The mid-day sun shone into my eyes and I tried to catch my friends. I climbed up the slide, hoping to tag someone at the top.	morning / (afternoon) / evening	garage / (playground) / store

28

Solutions

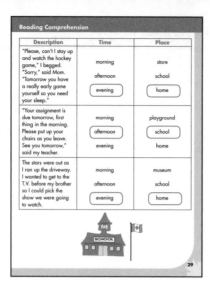

Page 29

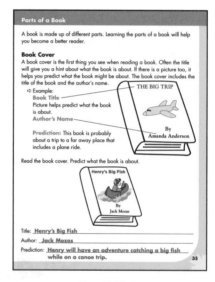

Page 31

Reading Comprehension (Page 29)

Description	Time	Place
"Please, can't I stay up and watch the hockey game," I begged. "Sorry," said Mom. "Tomorrow you have a really early game yourself so you need your sleep."	morning / afternoon / **evening**	store / school / **home**
"Your assignment is due tomorrow, first thing in the morning. Please put up your chairs as you leave. See you tomorrow," said my teacher.	morning / **afternoon** / evening	playground / **school** / home
The stars were out as I ran up the driveway. I wanted to get to the T.V. before my brother so I could pick the show we were going to watch.	morning / afternoon / **evening**	museum / school / **home**

Reading Comprehension (Page 31)

Fiction

After reading "A Trip to the Park," answer these questions. Write your answers in complete sentences.

Why was Matthew so nervous?

Matthew was nervous because the monkey bars were up high and they wobbled.

Why did Matthew start counting to himself?

Counting helped him think about what he needed to do to succeed.

Have you ever felt this way before trying something new? What did you do?

Answers will vary.

Do you think that having Daniel there helped Matthew complete the monkey bars? Why or why not?

Yes, Daniel helped Matthew by encouraging him. Matthew might not have tried the monkey bars if Daniel had not been there.

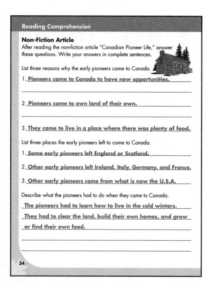

Page 34

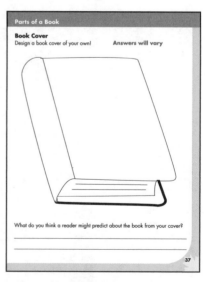

Page 35

Reading Comprehension (Page 34)

Non-Fiction Article

After reading the non-fiction article "Canadian Pioneer Life," answer these questions. Write your answers in complete sentences.

List three reasons why the early pioneers came to Canada.

1. Pioneers came to Canada to have new opportunities.
2. Pioneers came to own land of their own.
3. They came to live in a place where there was plenty of food.

List three places the early pioneers left to come to Canada.

1. Some early pioneers left England or Scotland.
2. Other early pioneers left Ireland, Italy, Germany, and France.
3. Other early pioneers came from what is now the U.S.A.

Describe what the pioneers had to do when they came to Canada.

The pioneers had to learn how to live in the cold winters. They had to clear the land, build their own homes, and grow or find their own food.

Parts of a Book (Page 35)

A book is made up of different parts. Learning the parts of a book will help you become a better reader.

Book Cover

A book cover is the first thing you see when reading a book. Often the title will give you a hint about what the book is about. If there is a picture too, it helps you predict what the book might be about. The book cover includes the title of the book and the author's name.

Example:
- Book Title — Picture helps predict what the book is about.
- Author's Name

Prediction: This book is probably about a trip to a far away place that includes a plane ride.

Read the book cover. Predict what the book is about.

Title: Henry's Big Fish

Author: Jack Mozas

Prediction: Henry will have an adventure catching a big fish while on a canoe trip.

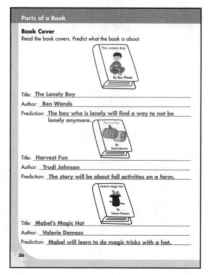

Page 36

Page 37

Parts of a Book (Page 36)

Book Cover

Read the book covers. Predict what the book is about.

Title: The Lonely Boy

Author: Ben Wands

Prediction: The boy who is lonely will find a way to not be lonely anymore.

Title: Harvest Fun

Author: Trudi Johnson

Prediction: The story will be about fall activities on a farm.

Title: Mabel's Magic Hat

Author: Valerie Demass

Prediction: Mabel will learn to do magic tricks with a hat.

Parts of a Book (Page 37)

Book Cover

Design a book cover of your own!   Answers will vary

What do you think a reader might predict about the book from your cover?

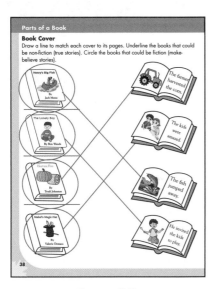

Page 38

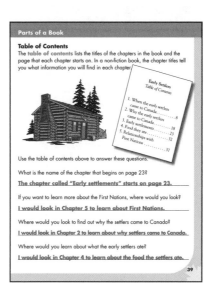

Page 39

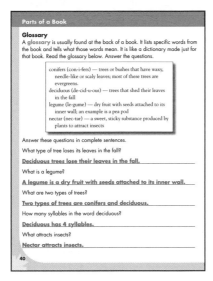

Page 40

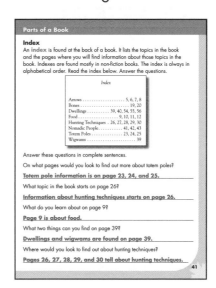

Page 41

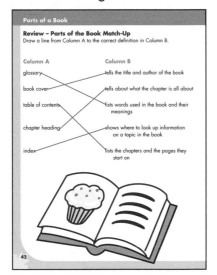

Page 42

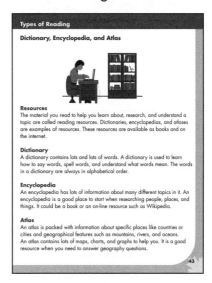

Page 43

Solutions

Page 44

Types of Reading

Research Skills

Read the following sentences. Write what resource you would use to answer the questions: dictionary, encyclopedia, or atlas?

↪ Example: Where is Ireland? __Atlas__

How do cars accelerate? __Encyclopedia__

What does the word "knight" mean? __Dictionary__

Where is the Atlantic Ocean? __Atlas__

Why do hummingbirds flap their wings so quickly? __Encyclopedia__

How many syllables are in the word "geography"? __Dictionary__

Who was Terry Fox and what did he do? __Encyclopedia__

Which country is south of Canada? __Atlas__

Did Canada fight in World War I? __Encyclopedia__

What does the word "apothecary" mean? __Dictionary__

Is "a-n-t" the correct way to spell the word that refers to a small insect?
__Dictionary__

Where is Victoria? __Atlas__

44

Page 44

Page 45

Types of Reading

Autobiographies

An **autobiography** is a book that tells the true story of a person's life. It is always written by the person who is the topic of the book. Answer the questions about yourself in complete sentences.

Answers will vary

Where were you born?

Who are the members of your family?

What activities do you like to do?

What is your favourite subject in school? Why is it your favourite?

What is your favourite television show? Why is it your favourite?

How many pets have you had? What kind of pet would you like to have now?

If you could do anything when you grow up, what would you like to do?

45

Page 45

Page 46

Types of Reading

Biographies

A **biography** is a book that tells the true story of a person's life. It is always written by a person who is not the topic of the book. It can be about someone who is alive now or someone who was alive a long time ago.
Examples of some biographies:

Terry Fox	Roberta Bondar	Mike Myers	Sidney Crosby
Athlete (Runner)	Astronaut	Entertainer	Athlete (Hockey Player)

Look at the biography examples. Answer these questions.
In which **biography** would you read about:

A person who has travelled in space?
__Roberta Bondar__

A person who has starred in movies?
__Mike Myers__

A person who spends lots of time on the ice?
__Sidney Crosby__

A person who likes to keep moving?
__Terry Fox__

Which biography would you like to read? Why?
__Answers will vary.__

46

Page 46

Page 47

Types of Reading

Reading a Letter

A **letter** is a form of communication between people.

August 29, 20XX

Dear Grandma,
I'm writing to let you know how my summer has been. It has been so long since I've seen you and I really miss our talks.
In July, I spent two weeks at camp. I had a great time swimming and canoeing. I met lots of new friends. August was spent at the cottage where I learned to play chess. It is a great game! I love sleeping in and having I Answers will vary ots of free time to do fun things.
School is nearly here. I'm not looking forward to getting up early every day or having homework to do at night. I hope to see you soon.

Lots of love,
Brad

Read the letter.
Answer each question with yes or no.

Did Brad like camp? __yes__
Is Brad looking forward to school? __no__
Did Brad learn to play chess? __yes__
Could Brad sleep in at the cottage? __yes__
Does Brad like to go canoeing? __yes__
Has Brad seen his Grandma lately? __no__

47

Page 47

Page 48

Types of Reading

Write a Letter

Write your own letter to a friend describing your last special family day.

Answers will vary.

48

Page 48

Page 49

Types of Reading

Posters

A **poster** is used to display information in words and pictures. It uses both words and pictures so the reader can understand the full meaning of the poster. Often important information is written in larger letters so that the reader can easily see it.

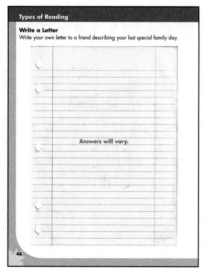

FOUND CAT
She was found at
11 Alberta Place on
Saturday, October 22

She has an orange coat with small patches of white on her belly.
Her eyes are blue and her tail is bent.

She is really friendly.

If she is yours please call:
Elaine at 416-555-1234

Read the poster. Circle the correct answer or answer the questions in complete sentences.

The cat is white (orange) grey
She has a bent whisker ear (tail)
She was found on (October 22) January 9 September 16
How can you reach the person who made the poster?
__Telephone the person who found the cat.__
Is the cat friendly?
__Yes__

49

Page 49

Page 50

Types of Reading

Advertisements and Flyers
Read the advertisement/flyer on the previous page.
Circle **true** or **false** after each sentence.

The jube jubes cost $1.99.	(true)	false
The lollipops used to be 50¢ each.	(true)	false
The licorice is the least expensive candy.	true	(false)
Chocolate bars are 89¢ on sale.	true	(false)
Jawbreakers are 3 for a dollar.	true	(false)
Gummy bears are less expensive than jube jubes.	true	(false)

Answer these questions in complete sentences.

What is your favourite kind of candy? Why is it your favourite?

Answers will vary.

Eating candy too much is not good for you. Why?

Answers will vary.

Page 52

Good job!

Written by teachers working in the Canadian classroom

Writing

Grade 3

CANADIAN CURRICULUM PRESS
Forward Learning

- Punctuation and grammar
- Ideas, planning, writing, editing
- Writing activities
- Cursive writing practice
- And much more!

Elaine J. Kenny, B.Ed.

Grade 3 Writing

Contents

Spelling Common Words

Knowing how to spell these common words will improve your writing!
Practice until you can spell each one correctly.

	Practice 1	Practice 2	Practice 3
about			
better			
bring			
carry			
clean			
done			
draw			
drink			
eight			
fall			
far			
full			
got			
grow			
hold			
hurt			
keep			

Good job!
You are half way there!

FINISH LINE

Spelling Common Words

	Practice 1	Practice 2	Practice 3
kind			
laugh			
light			
long			
much			
myself			
never			
only			
own			
pick			
seven			
shall			
show			
six			
small			
start			
ten			
today			
together			

FINISH LINE

You did it!
Way to go!

Words, Words, Words

Spelling Fun

Fifteen of the spelling words from pages 2 and 3 are a mixed-up mess! Unscramble the letters and write out each word correctly in the blank box.

#	Scrambled	
1.	rcayr	
2.	oabut	
3.	wadr	
4.	betert	
5.	atstr	
6.	grbni	
7.	hotrgtee	
8.	hgtie	
9.	eenvs	
10.	lnace	
11.	elfmsy	
12.	dnki	
13.	amwr	
14.	dnoe	
15.	ightl	

Spelling Word Search

```
H  R  B  Y  T  A  N  L  G  D  H  W  W  P  F
U  T  E  O  L  A  L  F  N  F  R  F  A  S  T
R  G  D  T  E  N  A  U  I  L  W  I  U  R  I
T  A  K  L  T  L  O  G  R  E  O  G  N  L  D
Y  N  C  I  L  E  N  L  B  S  H  R  H  K  L
A  A  A  G  N  O  B  M  E  Y  S  O  E  G  D
C  E  C  H  L  D  K  Y  H  M  S  W  O  N  L
U  I  E  T  M  U  C  H  U  G  P  M  E  G  O
L  G  R  E  H  T  E  G  O  T  U  V  A  L  H
R  H  D  S  N  E  V  E  S  R  E  A  L  L  M
R  T  E  N  O  D  S  T  A  R  T  A  L  R  L
U  P  I  C  K  C  A  R  R  Y  H  C  A  N  O
P  E  E  K  T  U  O  B  A  S  R  W  A  A  N
```

ABOUT	DRINK	KEEP	NEVER	START
BETTER	EIGHT	KIND	ONLY	TODAY
BRING	FALL	LAUGH	PICK	TOGETHER
CARRY	FULL	LIGHT	SEVEN	WARM
CLEAN	GROW	LONG	SHALL	
DONE	HOLD	MUCH	SHOW	
DRAW	HURT	MYSELF	SMALL	

5

Alphabetical Order

Alphabetical order is putting words in the order in which they appear in the alphabet.

 a b c d e f g h i j k l m n o p q r s t u v w x y z

Write the words in alphabetical order. If the first letters of two words are the same, look at the second letter in both words. If the second letters are the same in two words then look at the third letters.

Example:

 book

 bee

 balloon

Answer: 1. b<u>a</u>lloon   2. b<u>e</u>e   3. b<u>o</u>ok

 tree

 bush

 sun

 moon

 stars

1. _____   2. _____   3. _____   4. _____   5. _____

 watermelon

 apple

 pear

 peach

 plum

1. _____   2. _____   3. _____   4. _____   5. _____

Synonyms

Synonyms are words with nearly the same meaning.

Example: big ——→ large

big

large

Read each sentence. Fill in the blanks with the synonyms. The first one has been done for you.

little	large	rabbit	sleepy	jacket
frightening	complete	start	pal	sad

1. The **small** dog ran very fast. _____little_____

2. My favourite animal is a **bunny**. _____

3. We saw a **scary** movie. _____

4. After playing all day, I'm really **tired**. _____

5. I ate a **big** ice cream cone. _____

6. My **friend** and I love to play video games. _____

7. I can't wait to **begin** piano lessons. _____

8. I was **unhappy** when we lost our game. _____

9. Put on your **coat** before you go outside. _____

10. I hope I'm the first boy to **finish** the race. _____

Words, Words, Words

Antonyms

An **antonym** is a word that means the opposite of another word.

Example: hot ——→ cold

hot   cold

Read each word on the left. Match the word that has the opposite meaning.
Draw a line joining each pair of antonyms.

sad

hard

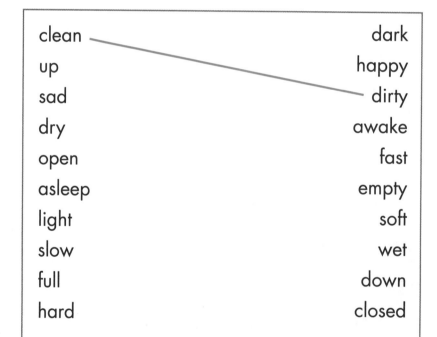

clean	dark
up	happy
sad	dirty
dry	awake
open	fast
asleep	empty
light	soft
slow	wet
full	down
hard	closed

happy

soft

Example: big ——→ small

big

small

Homophones

Homophones are words that sound the same, but have different meanings and are spelled differently.

Example:

cent

scent

Look at each picture. Underline the word that tells what the picture is.

weight wait

sun son

beat beet

see sea

flower flour

I eye

be bee

hair hare

write right

road rode

knight night

blew blue

bear bare

pear pair

Common Nouns

Common nouns are words that name a person, place, animal, or thing.

Examples: We are going skiing with our **friends**. (person)

We are skiing on a **mountain**. (place)

Sometimes we see **bears**. (animal)

Everyone wears a **helmet**. (thing)

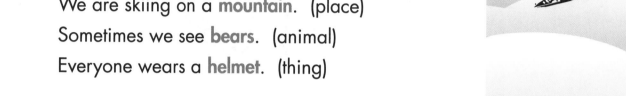

Read the common nouns below and then write them in the proper columns.

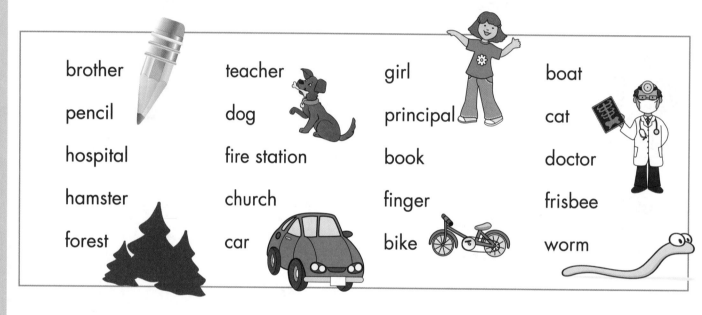

brother   teacher   girl   boat

pencil   dog   principal   cat

hospital   fire station book   doctor

hamster   church   finger   frisbee

forest   car   bike   worm

Person	Place	Animal	Thing

Proper Nouns

Proper nouns are the names of specific people, places, pets, or things. Proper nouns always begin with a capital letter. The days of the week and months of the year always begin with a capital letter.

Example: Proper noun: **Uncle Kevin** bought me a bike.
Common Noun: My **uncle** gave me a bike.

Read the sentences below. Rewrite each sentence and capitalize the proper nouns. The first one is done for you.

1. uncle deane lives in wiarton, ontario.

Uncle Deane lives in Wiarton, Ontario.

2. My birthday is in january.

3. justin bieber is my favourite singer.

4. In the summer I'm going to banff national park.

5. Four students in our class were born in july.

6. The toronto maple leafs play in the air canada centre.

7. My class is going to quebec city this june.

11

Parts of Speech

Pronouns

Pronouns take the place of a noun. They can be singular or plural.

Examples:

Type of Pronoun:	Singular:	Plural:
Pronouns used to talk about yourself.	I, me, my, mine	we, us, our, ours
Pronouns used to talk to someone else.	you, your, yours	you, your, yours
Pronouns used to talk about other people or things.	he, him, it, she, her, his, its	they, them, their, theirs

Underline the pronouns in each sentence.

1. <u>My</u> bike has streamers on <u>its</u> handlebars.

2. Dad told us to brush our teeth.

3. I watched a movie on the internet.

4. She bought a new sweater.

5. He told them to stop yelling.

Write each sentence again using a pronoun instead of the circled words.

1. Bender is (Jeffrey's) dog.
   Bender is **his** dog.

2. (Samantha) played volleyball at school today.

3. The (hamster's) wheel is too small.

Parts of Speech

Adjectives

An **adjective** is a word that describes a noun. Adjectives are used in the following situations:

1. to describe how many ⟶ **Example:** four kittens
2. to describe what kind ⟶ **Example:** blue sky
3. to describe which one(s) ⟶ **Example:** this house

Complete the sentences with an adjective that describes each picture.
The first one is done for you.

This is a **tall** tree.

Look at the
_____ flowers.

This bunny has
_____ ears.

This clown has a
_____ nose.

_____ is my
Dad's car.

This train is
_____.

My school is
_____.

My dog is
_____.

The house has a
_____ door.

13

Verbs

Verbs are words that show action and that something exists.

Examples: We **sailed** on Crystal Lake.
I **am** ten years old.

In each sentence below, circle the verbs.

 Example: We (went) to the library and (read) some books.

1. Amanda drew a picture with her new crayons.
2. Aiesha slipped on the ice and broke her leg.
3. Jamal looked through the window.
4. The chef baked delicious scones and muffins.
5. The girls ran and jumped over the fence.
6. The whole class laughed at my joke.
7. I lost my pencil in science class.
8. Read the second chapter by the end of the week.
9. The students wrote their answers on the board.
10. Grandma answered the door in her pyjamas.
11. Kevin shovelled the driveway.
12. Samantha washed and folded the laundry.
13. Jeff vacuumed the entire house.
14. Ken barbequed chicken for dinner.
15. Pull the blinds down before you go to bed.

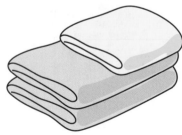

Past Tense Verbs

Past tense verbs tell something that has already happened.

To put most verbs in the past tense, add "**ed**" to the basic verb form:

cook ——→ cook**ed**   clean ——→ clean**ed**

When the verb ends in a silent "**e**," drop the "**e**" and add "**ed**":

rak**e** ——→ rak**ed**   hop**e** ——→ hop**ed**

When the verb ends in "**y**" after a consonant, change the "**y**" to an "**i**" and add "**ed**":

bur**y** ——→ bur**ied**   cr**y** ——→ cr**ied**

When the verb ends in a single consonant after a single short vowel, double the final consonant and add "**ed**":

chip ——→ chip**ped**   flip ——→ flip**ped**

Write the past tense of each of the following verbs using the correct "**ed**" ending. The first one is done for you.

laugh	bake	pop
laughed		
_____	_____	_____

| shovel | drop | answer |
| _____ | _____ | _____ |

| dance | plant | pull |
| _____ | _____ | _____ |

Adverbs

An **adverb** describes a verb. It answers the questions **How? When? Where?** about verbs.

How Adverbs

skillfully, sloppily, carefully, quickly, slowly, gently, roughly, crossly, nervously

When Adverbs

soon, never, always, yesterday, now, often, today, last, rarely, tomorrow

Where Adverbs

here, there, everywhere, away

Write an adverb on each line to complete the sentence. Make sure your adverb tells what is shown in the brackets. The first one is done for you.

1. Our plane leaves _____**tomorrow**_____.
   (when?)

2. Ava danced _____ at the recital.
   (how?)

3. We will go to the grocery store _____.
   (when?)

4. Come _____ to get your allowance.
   (where?)

5. We ran _____ so we wouldn't be late for school.
   (how?)

6. The bus will arrive _____.
   (when?)

7. The tree goes _____.
   (where?)

8. The juice spilled _____.
   (where?)

Subject

The **subject** of a sentence tells who or what the sentence is about. The subject does the action. It can be more than one word.

Example: A **beaver** swims in water.

Underline the subject in each sentence.

1. <u>Cows</u> are milked daily.

2. Robin's cat has lots of toys.

3. An apple tree grows in my backyard.

4. Raincoats keep us dry.

5. Mr. Stanley lost his car keys.

Predicate

The **predicate** is the part of the sentence that tells something about the subject. It can be more than one word.

Example: A beaver (swims in water)

Circle the predicate in each sentence.

1. Monkeys (swing from trees)

2. Whales swim in the ocean.

3. Our team won the championship.

4. My brother found twenty dollars.

5. Jeffrey is always looking for food.

17

Capital Letters

We use capital letters in many places:

1. At the beginning of every sentence.   **Example:** Are you hungry?

2. Proper nouns, like the specific names for people, places, and animals.
   Examples: Elaine Jane Kenny (person)
   Bender (animal name)
   Ottawa (place)

3. The word "I".   **Example:** I am reading.

4. Capital letters are used at the beginning of months, days, and holidays.
   Example: January, Monday, and Thanksgiving

5. Titles of books, TV programs, movies, poems, and documents.
   Note: Small words like "in," "and," "of," "if," "on" are not capitalized.
   Examples: Alice in Wonderland (book)
   Wizards of Waverly Place (TV program)
   Gnomeo and Juliet (movie)
   Alligator Pie (poem)

Rewrite the sentences below using capital letters where needed.

1. i swam in lake ontario when i was in toronto.
   I swam in Lake Ontario when I was in Toronto.
   _____

2. last monday, january 9th, was my birthday.

   _____

3. i visited halifax, nova scotia last summer.

   _____

4. valentine's day is celebrated on february 14th.

   _____

5. meg's volleyball team is travelling to calgary, alberta.

Capital Letters

Rewrite the book titles, TV programs, and movies below with proper capitals. Remember to always capitalize the first word and other important words, but not the small words (and, of, in, on, to).

Example:

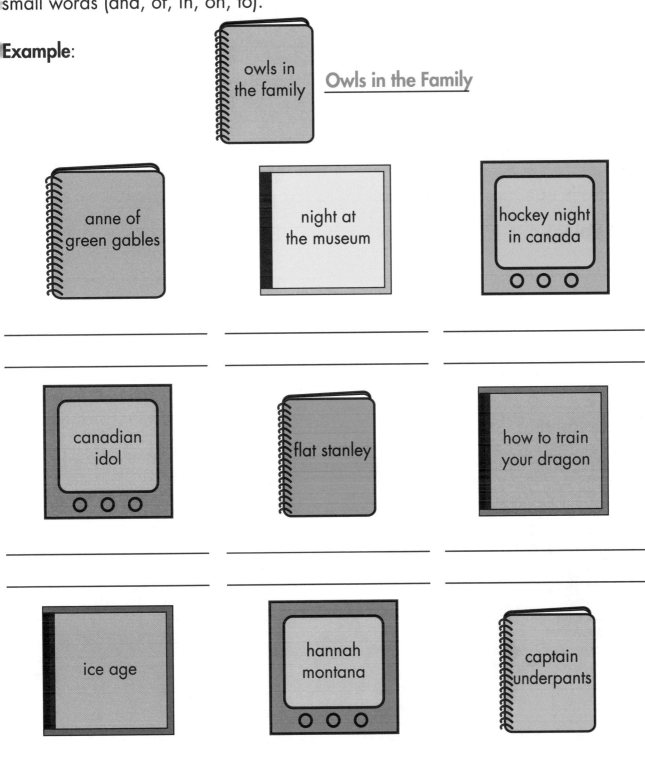

owls in the family   <u>Owls in the Family</u>

anne of green gables

night at the museum

hockey night in canada

_____

_____

canadian idol

flat stanley

how to train your dragon

_____

_____

ice age

hannah montana

captain underpants

_____

_____

Capital Letters

Complete each sentence using capital letters as needed. Don't forget the periods!

1. My name is _____

2. I was born in _____

3. I live in the city of _____, in the province of _____, in the country of _____

4. My favourite holiday is _____

5. My pet's name is _____

6. The names of my family members are_____

    _____

7. My favourite book is _____

8. My favourite movie is _____

9. My favourite song is _____

10. My favourite TV show is _____

11. My favourite teacher is _____

12. My school's name is _____

Periods

Periods come at the end of sentences. We use **periods** in the following ways:

1. At the end of a statement.   **Example:** I like to go shopping.
2. At the end of a command.   **Example:** Go to bed.
3. After an initial.   **Example:** Elaine J. Kenny
4. After an abbreviation.   **Examples of common abbreviations:**

Days:	Months:	Street Type:
Monday ⟶ Mon. Tuesday ⟶ Tues. Wednesday ⟶ Wed. Thursday ⟶ Thurs. Friday ⟶ Fri. Saturday ⟶ Sat. Sunday ⟶ Sun.	January ⟶ Jan. February ⟶ Feb. March ⟶ Mar. August ⟶ Aug. September ⟶ Sept. October ⟶ Oct. November ⟶ Nov. December ⟶ Dec.	Avenue ⟶ Ave. Boulevard ⟶ Blvd. Court ⟶ Crt. Crescent ⟶ Cres. Drive ⟶ Dr. Road ⟶ Rd. Street ⟶ St.

Rewrite the sentences by adding periods where needed below.

Example: Mr Stanley is my principal
                Mr. Stanley is my principal.

1. Kevin goes to Poplar Rd Jr PS

_____

2. Mr Samuel D Kenny is my uncle

_____

3. Mrs Black lives on Main St

_____

4. Wed, Aug 3rd

_____

5. Please pass the salt

_____

Statements and Questions

Statements are sentences that tell information. They always start with a capital and end in a period.

Questions are sentences that ask information. They always start with a capital and end with a question mark (?). Many of them begin with asking words like Do, Did, How, Who, What, Where, When, Why.

Add the final punctuation to these sentences.

1. What is your name ____

2. My favourite treat is chocolate ice cream ____

3. Do you like pizza ____

4. What did you do after school ____

5. I can run fast ____

6. Will you play catch with me ____

7. I got an "A" on my spelling test ____

8. Did you clean your room ____

9. Today is hot ____

Imagine you went to tour the fire station. Write 2 of your own statement sentences about the tour.

1. _____

2. _____

Write 2 questions your parents might ask you about the tour.

1. _____

2. _____

Commas

We use **commas** in the following situations:

- between parts of an address.
  Example: 5 My Street, Fredericton, New Brunswick

- in a list of three or more items.
  Example: soccer, basketball, and baseball

- between the day and year in a date.
  Example: January 9, 1967

- to separate a direct quote from the rest of the sentence.
  Example: Lisa said, "Come over at 9 pm."

- after the greeting and closing in a friendly letter.
  Examples: greeting = Dear Diane, closing = Sincerely, Greg

- before a coordinating conjunction (and, but, for, nor, or, so, yet) that joins two clauses.
  Example: She went to bed early, but was still tired in the morning.

- after an introductory phrase such as yes, no, sure, and well.
  Example: Sure, I will go to the movies with you.

- after each phrase in a sentence, that contains a series of three or more phrases.
  Example: Pick up the garbage, take it out, then come back for the recycling box.

In the sentences/situations below, place commas where needed.

1. Jake Jeff and Henry go to Scouts together.

2. I moved from Hamilton Ontario to Calgary Alberta.

3. Dear Marie
   How are you? I am fine.
   Love Elaine

4. Lisa asked "Is that a good recipe?"

5. Yesterday I broke my shoelace tore my shirt and lost my lunch bag.

6. Volleyball practices will be Tuesday Wednesday and Thursday.

Quotation Marks

We use **quotation marks** in several ways:

- before and after the words of a direct quotation.
  Example: Kevin asked, "When are you coming over?"
- around titles of short stories, chapter titles, reports, song titles, and poems.
  Example: Mia read "The Cat in the Hat."

In the sentences below, place quotation marks where needed.
The first one is done for you.

1. "Shut the door," mother said.

2. My favourite chapter is called The Smokey Forest.

3. Have you read the story called Mathmatickles?

4. Ahmed read a report titled, Canadian Wildlife.

5. Are you going to the movies? Samantha asked.

6. Andrea's report was titled Early Pioneers.

7. Free Willy is one of my favourite movies.

8. Have you heard the song One Less Lonely Girl?

9. Grandpa read me the story Green Eggs and Ham.

10. The poem In Flander's Field is about Remembrance Day.

11. Walter asked Raj, Are you coming for dinner?

Editing

Editing is checking over your rough copy to correct mistakes. You usually use a different colour pencil (red) when you edit so that you can easily see the corrections to make on your good copy.

Editing Marks

≡ capitalize
Example: the cat is black.

⊙ add a period
Example: My friend is here ⊙

② question mark missing
Example: Is he O.K. ②

◯ correct spelling
Example: The cow ⟨wis⟩ milked
earlier today. was

/ change to lower case
Example: I /ive in Calgary.

∧ add something
Example: The zebra∧black and
white. is

∧ add a comma
Example: I was born on January
9∧2000.

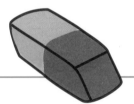

Edit the following paragraph. Use a red pencil and the marks above.

Mr. and Mrs davis have threa children. They live in a House in

red deer Alberta   Their children's names are peter lisa and alex.

The children go to charlottetown jr public schoon located on

Charlottetown Blvd. the family has two doggs and for Cats.

Whould you like to be part of the Davis family

Recount

A **recount** is retelling something that has happened. It is written in the order the events happened. Sometimes it is a personal recount about an experience that has happened to you. Other times it could be a factual recount of an event you have heard about, such as an accident or a newspaper report.

Recounts answer the following questions:

- When? — When did the event happen?
- Where? — Where did it take place?
- What? — What happened?
- Who? — Who was involved?
- Why? — Why did it happen?

Example:
Read the story. Use the chart to plan a recount. Then read the recount.

When?	Where?	What?	Who?	Why?
yesterday	at the library	went to take out books	my family	get some books for everyone to read

Title
summarizes the text →

Opening
tells when, who, where, and why →

A Trip to the Library

Yesterday my family went to the library to take out some books. When we got to the library we all split up to look in different areas. After finding what we were looking for, we all met up by the checkout counter. Before we left we checked out our books. When we got home we all went into our own rooms to read our new books.

Events
in order that they happened written in the past tense

Conclusion

Recount

Write your own recount. Plan your recount in the chart first.

When?	Where?	What?	Who?	Why?

Procedural Writing

Procedural writing includes directions about how to do a certain task in sequential order. Some examples are science experiments, game instructions, or recipes.

Example:

Topic:
- How to Make a Peanut Butter and Jam Sandwich

Aim/Goal: (what is the task?)
- Make a sandwich for lunch.

Requirements: (what is needed to complete the task?)
- 2 pieces of whole wheat bread
- peanut butter
- jam
- teaspoon
- butter knife
- plate
- cutting board

Method: (how to complete the task)
- Put 2 pieces of whole wheat bread on a cutting board.
- Using the butter knife, spread peanut butter evenly over 1 slice of bread.
- Using the teaspoon, scoop a spoonful of jam onto the peanut buttered bread and spread evenly with the butter knife.
- Put other slice of bread on top.
- Cut in half and put on a plate.
- Eat and enjoy!

Evaluation/Testing: (was the goal achieved?)
- Lunch was delicious!

Procedural Writing

Write your own procedural plan. Some topic suggestions: wrap a present, prepare a bowl of cereal, score a goal, or use your imagination and choose one of your own.

Topic:

_____

Aim/Goal:

_____

Requirements:

_____

_____

_____

_____

_____

Method:

_____

_____

_____

_____

_____

Evaluation/Testing:

_____

_____

Persuasive Paragraphs

In a **persuasive paragraph**, you are writing with the purpose of convincing your readers to believe in something, or take action about something. Examples of these include newspaper editorials and letters to the editor.

How to Write a Persuasive Paragraph:

Introduction ⟶ Begin with an interesting topic sentence. The topic sentence explains what the paragraph is all about.

Body ⟶ Next write 3 or 4 sentences explaining the reasons you have to back up your topic sentence.

Conclusion ⟶ In this sentence, repeat your opinion from the topic sentence, asking readers to agree with you or to take action.

Example:

**Introduction/
Topic Sentence** ⟶ Tearing down the school playground would be a terrible thing. The playground provides the students with something fun to do at recess, keeping them out of mischief. The playground also offers a way for students to keep active, improving their physical fitness levels. Many families use the playground after school as a way to meet and get to know other families in the community. Please come to the School Council meeting next Wednesday and speak up to save the playground!

Reasons Supporting Opinion

Conclusion

Plan Your Own Persuasive Paragraph

Think of something you feel really strongly about. Maybe you want to compost in the lunchroom to help eliminate some of the garbage going to landfills. Maybe you love animals and want to encourage people to take better care of their pets. Or perhaps you want to let everyone know how bad smoking is for his or her health.

Fill in the outline below to help you plan your persuasive paragraph.

Introduction
Topic sentence with opinions/feelings about the topic clearly stated

_____

_____

_____

Body
3 or 4 reasons and/or facts to back up your opinion

1. _____

2. _____

3. _____

4. _____

Conclusion
What should the reader do or believe?

_____

_____

_____

_____

Persuasive Paragraphs

Publish Your Persuasive Paragraph

Write a rough copy of your persuasive paragraph on a separate piece of paper. Edit your work for proper punctuation and spelling, then write the final copy here.

_____

_____

_____

_____

_____

_____

_____

_____

_____

_____

_____

_____

_____

_____

_____

**Share your writing with a friend or family member. Maybe you can
persuade them to feel the same way you do!**

Narratives

A **narrative** text tells an imaginative story. There are many different types of narratives and each one has its own set of characteristics.

Examples of Narrative Types (Just a Few!):

- **Myth/Legend** ⟶ A story handed down through tradition that explains an event or custom. Examples: *Robin Hood, King Arthur, Medusa, Hercules*

- **Fable** ⟶ A story written to teach a lesson that includes elements like a moral and animals with human characteristics. Examples: "Tortoise and the Hare," "Boy Who Cried Wolf," "Wolf in Sheep's Clothing"

- **Historical Fiction** ⟶ A story based on a historical event and/or the setting is historically based. Examples: *Anne of Green Gables, Underground to Canada*

- **Science Fiction** ⟶ A story often set in the future involving the effect of science and technology on society. Examples: *The Giver, Children of the Dust, Aliens Ate My Homework*

- **Fantasy** ⟶ A story that uses magic or the supernatural. Examples: *Harry Potter, Chronicles of Narnia, James and the Giant Peach*

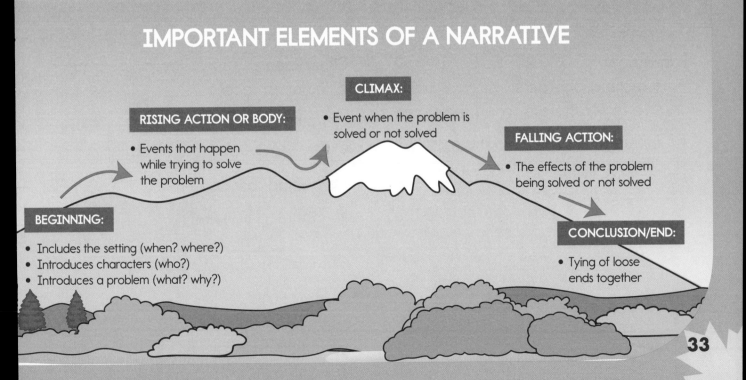

IMPORTANT ELEMENTS OF A NARRATIVE

CLIMAX:
- Event when the problem is solved or not solved

RISING ACTION OR BODY:
- Events that happen while trying to solve the problem

FALLING ACTION:
- The effects of the problem being solved or not solved

BEGINNING:
- Includes the setting (when? where?)
- Introduces characters (who?)
- Introduces a problem (what? why?)

CONCLUSION/END:
- Tying of loose ends together

Narratives

Plan Your Narrative

This is when you decide what your story is going to be about. Preplanning will make it easier for you to complete your story.

These are some suggestions for story topics:

Historical Fiction
- Choose a historical figure you know about and admire, Terry Fox, for example.
- Choose one of the sentences below and write a story explaining the figure's wishes, dreams, or fears:

    The saddest moment in life was when…
    My favourite childhood memory is…
    The thing that scared me the most was…

Realistic Fiction
- Create a character that has a secret to confess.
- Write about the events leading up to the secret and how that character resolves the problem created.

Fantasy
- Create a character, or a few, that live in a different world than ours.
- Include details about their daily life, history, and how they survive.

Other Ideas
- tales at recess
- camp adventures
- sports teams
- getting lost
- haunted house

Narratives

Get Started...

Fill in the story planner. Include details to help you write your story.

Characters
Who plays a role in your story?
Include descriptive details.

_____

_____

_____

Setting
Describe where and when
your story takes place.

_____

_____

Beginning

Problem
What are the characters trying to solve or overcome?

_____

_____

Body
What events happen while trying to solve the problem?

1. _____

_____

2. _____

_____

3. _____

_____

Middle

Resolution
Is the problem solved or not?

_____

_____

End

Narratives

First Draft

Write the first draft of your story.
Remember to use descriptive words to introduce your characters and setting. Make sure to have a clear problem and then work toward solving it.

Title: _____ **By:** _____

_____

_____

_____

_____

_____

_____

_____

_____

_____

_____

_____

_____

_____

_____

_____

_____

Narratives

Revise and Edit Your Story

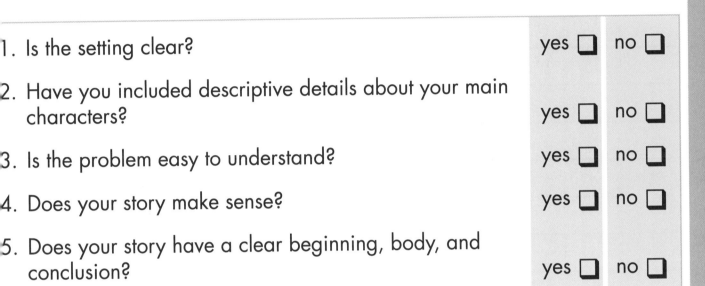

Look at the checklist below.
If any of the **no** boxes are checked, go back and add that detail to your story.

1. Is the setting clear?	yes ☐	no ☐
2. Have you included descriptive details about your main characters?	yes ☐	no ☐
3. Is the problem easy to understand?	yes ☐	no ☐
4. Does your story make sense?	yes ☐	no ☐
5. Does your story have a clear beginning, body, and conclusion?	yes ☐	no ☐

• Go back and add parts to your story to make it better!

After the changes are complete, it is time to **edit**.
This is when you reread your story looking for things that need fixing.

1. Make sure each sentence begins with a capital and ends with proper punctuation.

2. Check that all proper nouns begin with a capital letter.

3. Use quotation marks when someone is speaking.

4. Check for spelling mistakes.

Narratives

Time to Publish

Rewrite your story making sure to include all the changes you made.

_____

_____

_____

_____

_____

_____

_____

_____

_____

_____

_____

_____

_____

_____

_____

_____

_____

Poetry

There are many different types of poems. Some of them rhyme, and some of them don't.

Haiku

- A Japanese poem that follows a specific pattern.
- It is often about nature.
- It has three lines.
- The first line has five syllables.
- The second line has seven syllables.
- The third line has five syllables.

Example:

> Summertime is great   (5 syllables)
> We always spend time outdoors   (7 syllables)
> Basking in the sun   (5 syllables)

Shape Poem

- Creates an image with words

Example:

stem
stem
stem
stem
stem

worm
worm
worm
worm
worm
worm

apple apple
apple apple apple apple apple apple worm
apple apple apple apple apple apple apple
apple apple apple apple apple apple apple apple
apple apple apple apple apple apple apple apple
apple apple apple apple apple apple apple apple
apple apple apple apple apple apple apple apple
apple apple apple apple apple apple apple apple
apple apple apple apple apple apple apple apple
apple BRUISE apple apple apple apple apple
apple apple apple apple apple apple apple
apple apple apple apple apple apple apple
apple apple apple apple apple apple
apple apple apple apple apple apple
apple apple apple apple apple
apple apple apple apple apple
apple   apple apple   apple

Poetry

Lune

- A poem that follows a set of rules:
  Line 1 is three words
  Line 2 is five words
  Line 3 is three words

> **Example**:
>
> The flat tire (3 words)
> Stops us from going out (5 words)
> I'm so sad (3 words)

Acrostic

- The first letter of each line spells the subject of the poem.

> **Example:**
>
> **S** wimming in the lake
> **U** nder the bright blue sky
> **M** aking many
> **M** emories
> **E** veryone is
> **R** eally happy

Catalogue Poem

- Describes a person, place, or experience with a list of qualities for the topic

> **Example:**
>
> **School**
> School is a great place
> Meet new friends
> Learn new things
> Try different experiments
> Go on trips with classmates

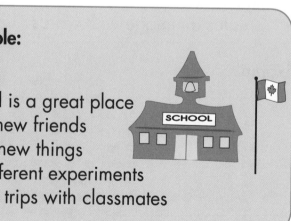

Poetry

Create Your Own Poems

Haiku

_____ (5 syllables)

_____ (7 syllables)

_____ (5 syllables)

Shape

Remember that your poem should create a shape with words.

Lune

_____ (3 words)

_____ (5 words)

_____ (3 words)

Poetry

Create Your Own Poems

Catalogue

_____

_____

_____

_____

_____

_____

_____

_____

Title

List of qualities describing the topic

Acrostic

_____

_____

_____

_____

_____

_____

_____

The first letter of each line spells the subject of the poem.

etters

etter writing is one of the oldest forms of communication. It has many purposes uch as to inform, to entertain, to express an opinion, or to persuade. In some ases, letters can be read over and over again and enjoyed for many years.

ypes of Letters:

. A **friendly letter** is like a long-distance conversation in writing. In this type of letter, you might share your thoughts and feelings, exciting news, or what's been happening in your life.

2. **E-mails** are usually friendly; however, they can be formal depending on the audience and purpose.

3. **Formal letters** are written for a number of reasons and are usually written to a business or organization. They might request information, give an opinion, look for a job, place an order, or make a complaint. These letters follow a specific format.

Letters

This is a sample of a friendly letter.

Return Address
Include this so your friend can send you a letter back.

Date
The date you wrote the letter.

Greeting
This is a way to start your letter. **Dear** and **Hi** are often used. Don't forget to capitalize your greeting and your friend's name and to end with a comma.

Body
The body of your letter is where you ask questions and tell about yourself. Don't forget to indent your first line!

Closing
This is a way to end your letter. Words like Goodbye, Sincerely, and Take care are often used. Don't forget your capital letter on the first word of your closing and a comma at the end of it!

Signature
Here is where you write your name so your friend knows who the letter is from.

---

123 Queen Street
Majesty, Ontario
M1G 4H9
August 15, 20XX

Dear Sam,

How has your summer been so far? I can't believe we go back to school in less than a month.

So far this summer I have gone to camp and spent a week at my aunt's house. I have been swimming a lot and can now dive off the diving board.

I can't wait to hear how your summer has been! See you at school in September. Please write back.

See you soon,

Jeffrey

Letters

Write a Friendly Letter

Remember to include the following:

- Return address and date
- Body
- Greeting (don't forget the comma!)
- Closing

_____

_____

_____

_____

_____,

_____

_____

_____

_____

_____

_____

_____

_____

_____,

_____

Letters

This is a sample of a formal letter.

Upper Address
Includes the writer's complete address.

Date
The date you wrote the letter.

Inside Address
Includes the name, title, and address of the receiver.

Greeting
This is a way to start your letter.

Body
The body of a formal letter is written in one or more paragraphs and clearly states the purpose and provides information.

Closing
This is a way to end your letter. The writer's full signature is included.

My Name
11 Your Road Street
Up North, Ontario
L0G 3E4
October 17, 20XX

Mr. Smith
Pioneer Times
987 Log Cabin Way
Wagonwheel, Ontario
L0G 1W2

Dear Mr. Smith,

My class is studying pioneers. I was using the internet to research log cabins and I read about a kit that you have that will teach me how to build a model of a log cabin. I would like to buy a copy. I am sending you a money order for $9.99 to cover the cost of the book.

Please send the kit to me at the above address.

Yours truly,
My Signature

My Name

Letters

Write a Formal Letter

Remember to include the following:

- Upper address
- Date
- Inside address
- Closing including your complete signature
- Body stating why you're writing the letter

Fables

Fables are stories that teach a lesson or moral. You have probably heard about many famous fables. Fables usually use animals as the main characters.

Read the fable called The Lion and the Mouse:

One day a small mouse ran over the foot of a big lion. The lion grabbed the mouse and the mouse shouted, "Please let me go, lion! If you let me go, I will help you in return one day." The lion replied, "How could a small mouse like you ever help a brave lion like me?" The lion thought this idea was so funny he started to laugh. He laughed so hard he let go of the mouse. "Who cares about a small mouse anyway," said the lion to himself. The following week the mouse was scurrying through the woods when he came across the lion, trapped in a hunter's ropes. The mouse thought, "I promised to help the lion, so I will." He began to chew the rope. He kept chewing until the ropes broke and the lion was freed. "Thank you! Thank you!" exclaimed the lion. "I was wrong to have teased you for being too small."

The moral of the story:
Even small friends can do big things.

Write your own fable.

Main characters: (If your main character is sly, you might choose a fox. If it is wise, you might choose an owl.)

_____

_____

Setting: (Where does your story take place? Is there more than one setting?)

_____

_____

_____

PLOT:
Beginning: (Introduce your characters. What happens in the beginning?)

_____

_____

_____

Middle: (What problem arises?)

_____

_____

_____

End: (How is the problem solved? What lesson is taught in this fable?)

_____

_____

Now that you have planned out your own fable write it out on page 58 or on a separate piece of paper.

Descriptive Writing

Descriptive writing is writing that describes people, places, objects, or events with creative details. In descriptive writing, details often evoke the five senses: sight, sound, smell, feel, or taste.

Your spaceship has just touched down on a mysterious planet and it is your job to report to earth about the aliens who live there. Luckily, you see a group of aliens near your spaceship. Answer the questions using describing words (adjectives) to explain what an alien is like.

Plan Your Description

What does the alien's head look like?

_____

_____

Does it have eyes, ears, a nose, and a mouth? What do they look like?

_____

_____

What does the alien's body look like? What colour is it? How big is it? What shape is it? Does it look rough or smooth?

_____

_____

_____

How do the aliens communicate? What sounds do they make? What do they smell like?

_____

_____

_____

Writing Your Own Descriptive Paragraph

Use the ideas listed in your plan to write a descriptive paragraph that tells about the aliens. Make sure to include a topic sentence and to use describing words.

_____

_____

_____

_____

_____

_____

_____

_____

_____

Draw a picture of the aliens.

Design a Poster

Example: This is a poster advertising a book sale.

Design Your Own Poster

Draft an outline for your event. Remember to include why someone should come to your event!

Name of event: _____

What will happen there: _____

When: _____

Where: _____

Picture ideas: _____

_____

_____

Types of Writing

Draw your poster here.

Cursive Writing

a b c d e f g h i j k l m n o p q r s t u v w x y z

A B C D E F G H I J K L M N O P Q R S T U V W X Y Z

Practice each group of letters.

1. ✏️ *a, d, g, c, q*

a a a

d d d

g g g

c c c

q q q

add

dad

2. ✏️ *i, u, w, t*

i i i

u u u

w w w

t t t

it

wig

54

Cursive Writing

a b c d e f g h i j k l m n o p q r s t u v w x y z

A B C D E F G H I J K L M N O P Q R S T U V W X Y Z

3. ✏️ *e, l, h, f, j, b*

e *e* *e*

l *l* *l*

h *h* *h*

f *f* *f*

j *j* *j*

b *b* *b*

fell

life

4. ✏️ *n, m, v, x*

n *n* *n*

m *m* *m*

v *v* *v*

x *x* *x*

maven

Cursive Writing

abcdefghijklmnopqrstuvwxyz

ABCDEFGHIJKLMNOPQRSTUVWXYZ

5. p, r, s, o, y, z, k

p p p

r r r

s s s

o o o

y y y

z z z

k k k

zipper

yellow

Cursive Writing

a b c d e f g h i j k l m n o p q r s t u v w x y z

A B C D E F G H I J K L M N O P Q R S T U V W X Y Z

6. ✏️ Capital letters

A A

B B

C C

D D

E E

F F

G G

H H

I I

J J

K K

L L

M M

N N

O O

P P

Q Q

R R

S S

T T

U U

V V

W W

X X

Y Y

Z Z

Cursive Writing Practice

a b c d e f g h i j k l m n o p q r s t u v w x y z
A B C D E F G H I J K L M N O P Q R S T U V W X Y Z

Use cursive writing to rewrite your fable or description of an alien.
Or write a completely new story using cursive writing.

Cursive Writing Practice

a b c d e f g h i j k l m n o p q r s t u v w x y z
A B C D E F G H I J K L M N O P Q R S T U V W X Y Z

Cursive Writing Practice

a b c d e f g h i j k l m n o p q r s t u v w x y z

A B C D E F G H I J K L M N O P Q R S T U V W X Y Z

Solutions

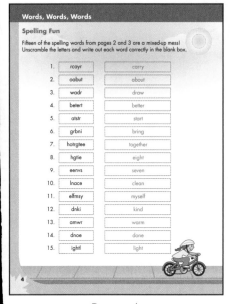

Words, Words, Words

Spelling Fun

Fifteen of the spelling words from pages 2 and 3 are a mixed-up mess! Unscramble the letters and write out each word correctly in the blank box.

1.	rcayr	carry
2.	oabut	about
3.	wadr	draw
4.	betert	better
5.	atstr	start
6.	grbni	bring
7.	hotrgtee	together
8.	hgtie	eight
9.	eenvs	seven
10.	lnace	clean
11.	elfmsy	myself
12.	dnki	kind
13.	amwr	warm
14.	dnoe	done
15.	ightl	light

Page 4

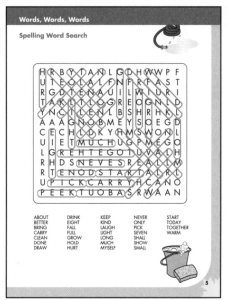

Words, Words, Words

Spelling Word Search

ABOUT	DRINK	KEEP	NEVER	START
BETTER	EIGHT	KIND	ONLY	TODAY
BRING	FALL	LAUGH	PICK	TOGETHER
CARRY	FULL	LIGHT	SEVEN	WARM
CLEAN	GROW	LONG	SHALL	
DONE	HOLD	MUCH	SHOW	
DRAW	HURT	MYSELF	SMALL	

Page 5

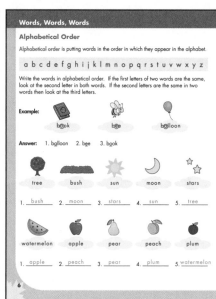

Words, Words, Words

Alphabetical Order

Alphabetical order is putting words in the order in which they appear in the alphabet.

a b c d e f g h i j k l m n o p q r s t u v w x y z

Write the words in alphabetical order. If the first letters of two words are the same, look at the second letter in both words. If the second letters are the same in two words then look at the third letters.

Example:

book   bee   balloon

Answer: 1. balloon 2. bee 3. book

tree   bush   sun   moon   stars

1. bush 2. moon 3. stars 4. sun 5. tree

watermelon   apple   pear   peach   plum

1. apple 2. peach 3. pear 4. plum 5. watermelon

Page 6

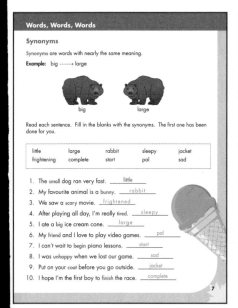

Words, Words, Words

Synonyms

Synonyms are words with nearly the same meaning.

Example: big ——→ large

big   large

Read each sentence. Fill in the blanks with the synonyms. The first one has been done for you.

little	large	rabbit	sleepy	jacket
frightening	complete	start	pal	sad

1. The small dog ran very fast. little
2. My favourite animal is a bunny. rabbit
3. We saw a scary movie. frightened
4. After playing all day, I'm really tired. sleepy
5. I ate a big ice cream cone. large
6. My friend and I love to play video games. pal
7. I can't wait to begin piano lessons. start
8. I was unhappy when we lost our game. sad
9. Put on your coat before you go outside. jacket
10. I hope I'm the first boy to finish the race. complete

Page 7

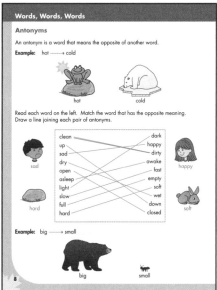

Words, Words, Words

Antonyms

An antonym is a word that means the opposite of another word.

Example: hot ——→ cold

hot   cold

Read each word on the left. Match the word that has the opposite meaning. Draw a line joining each pair of antonyms.

clean	dark
up	happy
sad	dirty
dry	awake
open	fast
asleep	empty
light	soft
slow	wet
full	down
hard	closed

sad   happy   hard   soft

Example: big ——→ small

big   small

Page 8

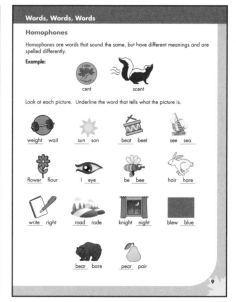

Words, Words, Words

Homophones

Homophones are words that sound the same, but have different meanings and are spelled differently.

Example:

cent   scent

Look at each picture. Underline the word that tells what the picture is.

weight <u>wait</u>   sun <u>son</u>   <u>beat</u> beet   see <u>sea</u>

<u>flower</u> flour   I <u>eye</u>   be <u>bee</u>   hair <u>hare</u>

<u>write</u> right   road <u>rode</u>   knight <u>night</u>   blew <u>blue</u>

bear <u>bare</u>   <u>pear</u> pair

Page 9

Solutions

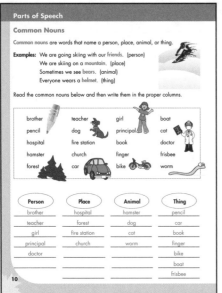

Common Nouns

Common nouns are words that name a person, place, animal, or thing.

Examples: We are going skiing with our friends. (person)
We are skiing on a mountain. (place)
Sometimes we see bears. (animal)
Everyone wears a helmet. (thing)

Read the common nouns below and then write them in the proper columns.

brother	teacher	girl	boat
pencil	dog	principal	cat
hospital	fire station	book	doctor
hamster	church	finger	frisbee
forest	car	bike	worm

Person	Place	Animal	Thing
brother	hospital	hamster	pencil
teacher	forest	dog	car
girl	fire station	cat	book
principal	church	worm	finger
doctor			bike
			boat
			frisbee

10

Page 10

Proper Nouns

Proper nouns are the names of specific people, places, pets, or things. Proper nouns always begin with a capital letter. The days of the week and months of the year always begin with a capital letter.

Example: Proper noun: Uncle Kevin bought me a bike.
Common Noun: My uncle gave me a bike.

Read the sentences below. Rewrite each sentence and capitalize the proper nouns. The first one is done for you.

1. uncle deane lives in wiarton, ontario.
Uncle Deane lives in Wiarton, Ontario.

2. My birthday is in january.
My birthday is in January.

3. justin bieber is my favourite singer.
Justin Bieber is my favourite singer.

4. In the summer I'm going to banff national park.
In the summer I'm going to Banff National Park.

5. Four students in our class were born in july.
Four students in our class were born in July.

6. The toronto maple leafs play in the roger's centre.
The Toronto Maple Leafs play in the Roger's Centre.

7. My class is going to quebec city this june.
My class is going to Quebec City this June.

11

Page 11

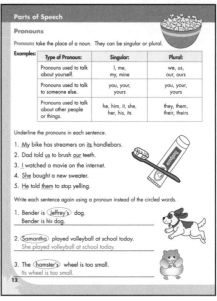

Pronouns

Pronouns take the place of a noun. They can be singular or plural.

Examples:

Type of Pronoun:	Singular:	Plural:
Pronouns used to talk about yourself.	I, me, my, mine	we, us, our, ours
Pronouns used to talk to someone else.	you, your, yours	you, your, yours
Pronouns used to talk about other people or things.	he, him, it, she, her, his, its	they, them, their, theirs

Underline the pronouns in each sentence.

1. My bike has streamers on its handlebars.
2. Dad told us to brush our teeth.
3. I watched a movie on the internet.
4. She bought a new sweater.
5. He told them to stop yelling.

Write each sentence again using a pronoun instead of the circled words.

1. Bender is Jeffrey's dog.
Bender is his dog.

2. Samantha played volleyball at school today.
She played volleyball at school today.

3. The hamster's wheel is too small.
Its wheel is too small.

12

Page 12

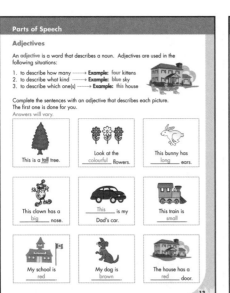

Adjectives

An adjective is a word that describes a noun. Adjectives are used in the following situations:

1. to describe how many → **Example:** four kittens
2. to describe what kind → **Example:** blue sky
3. to describe which one(s) → **Example:** this house

Complete the sentences with an adjective that describes each picture. The first one is done for you.
Answers will vary.

This is a **tall** tree.

Look at the **colourful** flowers.

This bunny has **long** ears.

This clown has a **big** nose.

This is my Dad's car.

This train is **small**.

My school is **red**.

My dog is **brown**.

The house has a **red** door.

13

Page 13

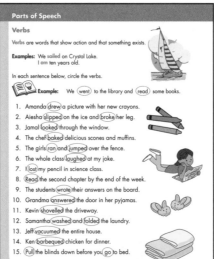

Verbs

Verbs are words that show action and that something exists.

Examples: We sailed on Crystal Lake.
I am ten years old.

In each sentence below, circle the verbs.

Example: We went to the library and read some books.

1. Amanda drew a picture with her new crayons.
2. Aiesha slipped on the ice and broke her leg.
3. Jamal looked through the window.
4. The chef baked delicious scones and muffins.
5. The girls ran and jumped over the fence.
6. The whole class laughed at my joke.
7. I lost my pencil in science class.
8. Read the second chapter by the end of the week.
9. The students wrote their answers on the board.
10. Grandma answered the door in her pyjamas.
11. Kevin shovelled the driveway.
12. Samantha washed and folded the laundry.
13. Jeff vacuumed the entire house.
14. Ken barbequed chicken for dinner.
15. Pull the blinds down before you go to bed.

14

Page 14

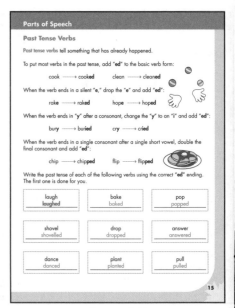

Past Tense Verbs

Past tense verbs tell something that has already happened.

To put most verbs in the past tense, add "ed" to the basic verb form:

cook → cooked   clean → cleaned

When the verb ends in a silent "e," drop the "e" and add "ed":

rake → raked   hope → hoped

When the verb ends in "y" after a consonant, change the "y" to an "i" and add "ed":

bury → buried   cry → cried

When the verb ends in a single consonant after a single short vowel, double the final consonant and add "ed":

chip → chipped   flip → flipped

Write the past tense of each of the following verbs using the correct "ed" ending. The first one is done for you.

laugh laughed	bake baked	pop popped
shovel shovelled	drop dropped	answer answered
dance danced	plant planted	pull pulled

15

Page 15

Page 16

Parts of Speech

Adverbs

An adverb describes a verb. It answers the questions How? When? Where? about verbs.

How Adverbs
skillfully, sloppily, carefully, quickly, slowly, gently, roughly, crossly, nervously

When Adverbs
soon, never, always, yesterday, now, often, today, last, rarely, tomorrow

Where Adverbs
here, there, everywhere, away

Write an adverb on each line to complete the sentence. Make sure your adverb tells what is shown in the brackets. The first one is done for you.

1. Our plane leaves ___tomorrow___ (when?)
2. Ava danced ___skillfully___ at the recital. (how?)
3. We will go to the grocery store ___tomorrow___ (when?)
4. Come ___here___ to get your allowance. (where?)
5. We ran ___quickly___ so we wouldn't be late for school. (how?)
6. The bus will arrive ___soon___ (when?)
7. The tree goes ___here___ (where?)
8. The juice spilled ___everywhere___ (where?)

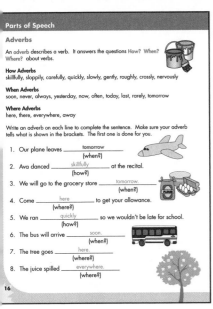

16

Page 17

Parts of Speech

Subject

The subject of a sentence tells who or what the sentence is about. The subject does the action. It can be more than one word.

Example: A <u>beaver</u> swims in water.

Underline the subject in each sentence.

1. <u>Cows</u> are milked daily.
2. <u>Robin's cat</u> has lots of toys.
3. <u>An apple tree</u> grows in my backyard.
4. <u>Raincoats</u> keep us dry.
5. <u>Mr. Stanley</u> lost his car keys.

Predicate

The predicate is the part of the sentence that tells something about the subject. It can be more than one word.

Example: A beaver (swims in water)

Circle the predicate in each sentence.

1. Monkeys (swing from trees)
2. Whales (swim in the ocean)
3. Our team (won the championship)
4. My brother (found twenty dollars)
5. Jeffrey (is always looking for food)

17

Page 18

Punctuation

Capital Letters

We use capital letters in many places:

1. At the beginning of every sentence. **Example:** Are you hungry?
2. Proper nouns, like the specific names for people, places, and animals.
   Examples: Elaine Jane Kenny (person)
   Bender (animal name)
   Ottawa (place)
3. The word "I". **Example:** I am reading.
4. Capital letters are used at the beginning of months, days, and holidays.
   Example: January, Monday, and Thanksgiving
5. Titles of books, TV programs, movies, poems, and documents.
   Note: Small words like "in," "and," "of," "if," "on" are not capitalized.
   Examples: Alice in Wonderland (book)
   Wizards of Waverly Place (TV program)
   Gnomeo and Juliet (movie)
   Alligator Pie (poem)

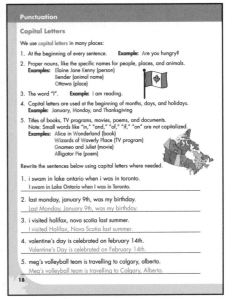

Rewrite the sentences below using capital letters where needed.

1. i swam in lake ontario when i was in toronto.
   I swam in Lake Ontario when I was in Toronto.
2. last monday, january 9th, was my birthday.
   Last Monday, January 9th, was my birthday.
3. i visited halifax, nova scotia last summer.
   I visited Halifax, Nova Scotia last summer.
4. valentine's day is celebrated on february 14th.
   Valentine's Day is celebrated on February 14th.
5. meg's volleyball team is travelling to calgary, alberta.
   Meg's volleyball team is travelling to Calgary, Alberta.

18

Page 19

Punctuation

Capital Letters

Rewrite the book titles, TV programs, and movies below with proper capitals. Remember to always capitalize the first word and other important words, but not the small words (and, of, in, on, to).

Example:

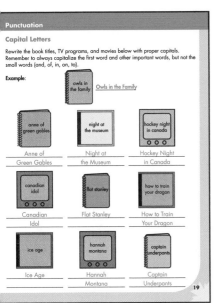

owls in the family → Owls in the Family

anne of green gables	night at the museum	hockey night in canada
Anne of Green Gables	Night at the Museum	Hockey Night in Canada
canadian idol	flat stanley	how to train your dragon
Canadian Idol	Flat Stanley	How to Train Your Dragon
ice age	hannah montana	captain underpants
Ice Age	Hannah Montana	Captain Underpants

19

Page 20

Punctuation

Capital Letters

Complete each sentence using capital letters as needed. Don't forget the periods!

1. My name is ___Answers will vary.___
2. I was born in _____
3. I live in the city of _____, in the province of _____, in the country of _____
4. My favourite holiday is _____
5. My pet's name is _____
6. The names of my family members are_____
7. My favourite book is _____
8. My favourite movie is _____
9. My favourite song is _____
10. My favourite TV show is _____
11. My favourite teacher is _____
12. My school's name is _____

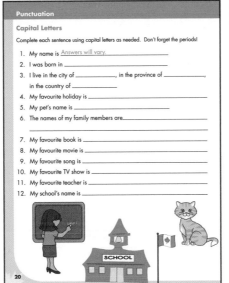

20

Page 21

Punctuation

Periods

Periods come at the end of sentences. We use periods in the following ways:

1. At the end of a statement. **Example:** I like to go shopping.
2. At the end of a command. **Example:** Go to bed.
3. After an initial. **Example:** Elaine J. Kenny
4. After an abbreviation. **Examples of common abbreviations:**

Days:	Months:	Street Type:
Monday → Mon.	January → Jan.	Avenue → Ave.
Tuesday → Tues.	February → Feb.	Boulevard → Blvd.
Wednesday → Wed.	March → Mar.	Court → Crt.
Thursday → Thurs.	August → Aug.	Crescent → Cres.
Friday → Fri.	September → Sept.	Drive → Dr.
Saturday → Sat.	October → Oct.	Road → Rd.
Sunday → Sun.	November → Nov.	Street → St.
	December → Dec.	

Rewrite the sentences by adding periods where needed below.

Example: Mr Stanley is my principal
Mr. Stanley is my principal.

1. Kevin goes to Poplar Rd Jr PS
   Kevin goes to Poplar Rd. Jr. P.S.
2. Mr Samuel D Kenny is my uncle
   Mr. Samuel D. Kenny is my uncle.
3. Mrs Black lives on Main St
   Mrs. Black lives on Main St.
4. Wed, Aug 3rd
   Wed., Aug. 3.
5. Please pass the salt
   Please pass the salt.

21

Solutions

Statements and Questions

Statements are sentences that tell information. They always start with a capital and end in a period.

Questions are sentences that ask information. They always start with a capital and end with a question mark (?). Many of them begin with asking words like Do, Did, How, Who, What, Where, When, Why.

Add the final punctuation to these sentences.

1. What is your name **?**
2. My favourite treat is chocolate ice cream **.**
3. Do you like pizza **?**
4. What did you do after school **?**
5. I can run fast **.**
6. Will you play catch with me **?**
7. I got an "A" on my spelling test **.**
8. Did you clean your room **?**
9. Today is hot **.**

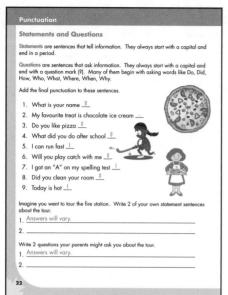

Imagine you went to tour the fire station. Write 2 of your own statement sentences about the tour.

1. Answers will vary.
2. _____

Write 2 questions your parents might ask you about the tour.

1. Answers will vary.
2. _____

22

Page 22

Commas

We use commas in the following situations:

- between parts of an address.
  Example: 5 My Street, Fredericton, New Brunswick
- in a list of three or more items.
  Example: soccer, basketball, and baseball
- between the day and year in a date.
  Example: January 9, 1967
- to separate a direct quote from the rest of the sentence.
  Example: Lisa said, "Come over at 9 pm."
- after the greeting and closing in a friendly letter.
  Examples: greeting = Dear Diane, closing = Sincerely, Greg
- before a coordinating conjunction (and, but, for, nor, or, so, yet) that joins two clauses.
  Example: She went to bed early, but was still tired in the morning.
- after an introductory phrase such as yes, no, sure, and well.
  Example: Sure, I will go to the movies with you.
- after each phrase in a sentence, that contains a series of three or more phrases.
  Example: Pick up the garbage, take it out, then come back for the recycling box.

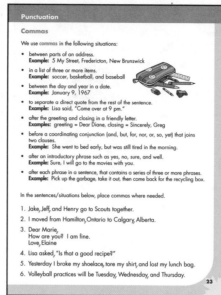

In the sentences/situations below, place commas where needed.

1. Jake, Jeff, and Henry go to Scouts together.
2. I moved from Hamilton, Ontario to Calgary, Alberta.
3. Dear Marie,
   How are you? I am fine.
   Love, Elaine
4. Lisa asked, "Is that a good recipe?"
5. Yesterday I broke my shoelace, tore my shirt, and lost my lunch bag.
6. Volleyball practices will be Tuesday, Wednesday, and Thursday.

23

Page 23

Quotation Marks

We use quotation marks in several ways:

- before and after the words of a direct quotation.
  Example: Kevin asked, "When are you coming over?"
- around titles of short stories, chapter titles, reports, song titles, and poems.
  Example: Mia read "The Cat in the Hat."

In the sentences below, place quotation marks where needed. The first one is done for you.

1. "Shut the door," mother said.
2. My favourite chapter is called "The Smokey Forest."
3. Have you read the story called "Mathmatickles?"
4. Ahmed read a report titled, "Canadian Wildlife."
5. "Are you going to the movies?" Samantha asked.
6. Andrea's report was titled "Early Pioneers."
7. "Free Willy" is one of my favourite movies.
8. Have you heard the song "One Less Lonely Girl?"
9. Grandpa read me the story "Green Eggs and Ham."
10. The poem "In Flander's Field" is about Remembrance Day.
11. Walter asked Raj, "Are you coming for dinner?"

24

Page 24

Editing

Editing is checking over your rough copy to correct mistakes. You usually use a different colour pencil (red) when you edit so that you can easily see the corrections to make on your good copy.

Editing Marks

≡ capitalize **Example:** the cat is black.	/ change to lower case **Example:** I Live in Calgary.
⊙ add a period **Example:** My friend is here ⊙	∧ add something **Example:** The zebra black and white. is
⑨ question mark missing **Example:** Is he O.K. ⑨	∧ add a comma **Example:** I was born on January 9, 2000.
◯ correct spelling **Example:** The cow wis milked earlier today. was	

Edit the following paragraph. Use a red pencil and the marks above.

Mr. and Mrs. davis have three children. They live in a House in
three
red deer, Alberta. Their children's names are peter, lisa and alex.
The children go to charlottetown jr. public school located on
school
Charlottetown Blvd. the family has two doggs and for Cats.
dogs four
Whould you like to be part of the Davis family?
Would

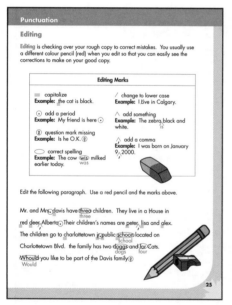

25

Page 25